£11·95

HAZARDOUS BUILDING MATERIALS

A guide to the selection of alternatives

HAZARDOUS BUILDING MATERIALS

A guide to the selection of alternatives

Edited by
S.R. Curwell & C.G. March

E. & F.N. Spon
LONDON

First published in 1986 by
E. & F.N. Spon Ltd
11 New Fetter Lane, London EC4P 4EE

© 1986 Fernsheer Ltd

Printed in Great Britain at the
University Press, Cambridge

ISBN 0 419 13730 0 (cased edition)
ISBN 0 419 13740 8 (paperback edition)

British Library Cataloguing in Publication Data

Hazardous building materials: a guide to the
    selection of alternatives.
    1. Building materials — Safety measures
    I. Curwell, S.R.   II. March, C.G.
    690'.22   TA403.6

    ISBN 0-419-13730-0
    ISBN 0-419-13740-8 Pbk

Contents

Section I **Introduction**

1

Professor R.A. Burgess, S.R. Curwell, C.G. March, University of Salford

Factors influencing dose or exposure — health hazard assessment — ventilation — technical and aesthetic assessment — building costs — use of guide — future considerations — disclosure of information

Section II **Hazards to health from building materials**

Asbestos and other natural materials
Dr M. Greenberg, Independent Consultant
Asbestos — a brief history of asbestos in modern times — asbestos in buildings — the effects of asbestos on health — relative risk of fibre types — waste disposal — use of asbestos in domestic buildings — timber — cellulose fibre — calcium silicate board — mineral fibre — vermiculite — natural slate — concrete slate — phosphogypsum

Man-made mineral fibres
J. Dodgson, The Institute of Occupational Medicine, Edinburgh
Introduction — physical and chemical properties of fibres — a brief history — types of MMMF — health effects — domestic usage of MMMF materials

Metals
Dr R.M. Harrison, Reader in Environmental Chemistry and Aerosol Science, University of Essex
Introduction — toxicology of aluminium — zinc — iron, steel and stainless steel — copper — lead — chromium — use of metals in domestic buildings

Lead in building materials
Dr M.F. Cuthbert, Professor A.N. Worden, Cantab Group
Introduction — health effects — sources of lead — paint — other uses

Plastics and toxic chemicals
Dr K. Fletcher, Independent Consultant
Plastics — introduction — toxicity — ingestion hazard — inhalation hazard — composites — toxic chemicals — wood preservatives — inhalation risk — adhesives

Contributors

Dr W. Allen
Senior Partner, Bickerdike Allen Partners

Professor R.A. Burgess
University of Salford

S.R. Curwell
University of Salford

Dr M.F. Cuthbert
Cantab Group

J. Dodgson
The Institute of Occupational Medicine, Edinburgh

Dr K. Fletcher
Independent Consultant

R.C. Fox
E.C. Harris and Partners

Dr M. Greenberg
Independent Consultant

Dr R.M. Harrison
Reader in Environmental Chemistry and Aerosol Science, University of Essex

C.G. March
University of Salford

Professor A.N. Worden
Cantab Group

Foreword

Science, the power tool of the modern mind, has changed fundamentally the ways in which we have to think about design and construction for it creates knowledge relevant to our work, and when this is published in appropriate ways and places its mere existence begins to generate liability for us to know and use it.

A great deal can and is being said and written which qualifies in various ways the blunt brutality of this truth of our times, but truth it is and remains all the same, gradually changing our habits of thought and action in design, specification and site work. And not just by fear of litigation, though that is real enough, but by its constructive appeal to the sense of responsibility in us as responsible people in the building industry.

We are not yet very familiar with the general idea that building materials can be hazards to health though we have known for quite a time now about the toxicity of lead in the form of plumbing and lead-based paints and more recently we have come to terms with the need to give up using asbestos. But these have been isolated risks, not part of a generalized understanding that health hazards are now among the criteria by which we should appraise the materials we select for use in our buildings. That is the valuable idea around which this book has been written.

William Allen
Bickerdike Allen Partners
London, England 1985

Preface

The considerable scientific and technological advances of this century have led to many benefits for mankind, but with them have also come fresh threats to health and well-being, the most notable being cancer. Professor Sir Richard Doll states in his preface to *Atlas of Cancer Mortality in England and Wales 1968–1978*, "On a world-wide scale the differences in incidence (of cancer) that have been observed encourage the belief that all the common types of cancer are largely avoidable, in the sense that it should be possible to reduce the risk of developing each type by at least a half and often by 80 per cent or more." The mark of a caring and responsible society is its determination to strike a balance between seizing all the opportunities of this advance and at the same time paying whatever price is necessary to ensure that it carries no dangers to ourselves or succeeding generations.

I find it appalling that our children can actually be harmed by deleterious substances without ever leaving their homes. We now know that many modern diseases and illnesses are caused by environmental factors. We now know what some of those environmental factors are. Much of the paintwork in our housing is still heavily leaded, and a threat to the mental well being of our children; many of whom receive their everyday drinking water from old leaded pipes. There is, too, the threatening presence in many homes of considerable quantities of asbestos. It has been estimated that 4 million of Britain's 4.5 million council homes are likely to contain asbestos, as are 80% of metropolitan schools and colleges, and 77% of social service buildings.

I have been proud to be associated with the developing movement in the UK concerned with conservation and environmental protection, but I have been convinced that to support these concerned organizations is not enough. We have to act with social responsibility in our own businesses and places of work, for this is where plans and decisions are made which, without adequate care, can lead to environmental destruction. That is why, in my own business, I have sought to ensure that great care be taken in the selection of safe and suitable building materials, and that it is recognized that we owe to people buildings which are safe environmentally as well as structurally.

I commissioned this work to draw together accumulated knowledge in different disciplines to help in the selection and evaluation of more safe and suitable building materials. I am pleased to share it with all those who are building the next generation of homes. It can, at best, be only a beginning, but I hope that all the various authorities will themselves undertake further research and offer continually updated guidance.

I hope, too, other organizations providing buildings will share my concern. Ignorance may be an excuse for what has happened in the past. This book, and the work that I hope will follow, should make it an unacceptable defence from now on. On a principle as old and simple as the golden rule itself, we all have a responsibility for the health and well-being of others.

Godfrey Bradman
London 1985

Acknowledgement

The research project which has culminated in the publication of this guide arose from the concern of Mr Godfrey Bradman about environmental pollution and we gratefully acknowledge his initiative, his funding of the project, and his encouragement to all involved.

Further acknowledgements

We wish to record our appreciation to E.C. Harris and Partners, Chartered Quantity Surveyors, for their efforts in providing all the cost information in Section III, which, although seemingly a small part in the text, disguises the full extent of the contribution.

We would also like to express our thanks to:

Mr G. Deakin, Warrington Research Centre, for his contribution on matters associated with fire.

Mr E. King, Director of the National Occupational Hygiene Services Ltd, for his support and advice throughout.

Dr A. Wrixon, National Radiological Protection Board, for his assistance in matters pertaining to radon.

Dr C.E. Miller, University of Salford, for his assistance and contribution on the same topic in Section II 2.9.

Dr P. Warren, Building Research Establishment, for his assistance on ventilation in the introduction.

Mr M. Eastwood for his advice and help, particularly on Section IV.

Finally, our thanks are due to the manufacturers who co-operated in supplying detailed information on their products.

SECTION I

INTRODUCTION

1 Introduction

R. A. BURGESS, BArch ARIBA PPCIOB FIMS MBIM
S. R. CURWELL, BSc MSc ARIBA
C. G. MARCH, BSc MCIOB

This guide is concerned with the deleterious effect which materials used in the construction of buildings may have on the health of users and occupiers. *The Concise Oxford Dictionary* defines deleterious as 'being harmful to mind or body', a clear and precise definition particularly appropriate when applied to some of the materials such as asbestos and lead used in the construction of buildings. The relative risk to the occupant's health depends upon individual applications of these materials together with other environmental factors within buildings — notably ventilation. There are substitute materials available, but unfortunately these also may have some risk attached to their use.

The problem for the building designer is to select materials which offer the least hazard to health but are still technically and aesthetically satisfactory and remain within sensible cost limits. It is hoped that this guide will assist him or her in this task.

Problems arising in existing buildings and from maintenance and alterations carried out particularly by the DIY occupier are also taken into account.

The last three decades have seen a revolution in science and medicine leading to a much clearer understanding of nature and of the human condition so that the effects of environmental factors and their relationship to health are more clearly appreciated.

The main concern in the recent past has concentrated upon the operational exposure of the workforce involved in manufacture and the processing industries which has led to a general improvement in working conditions. Concern shown over deleterious materials at the workplace has, quite rightly, developed together with an increasing awareness of the problems over pollution in the environment from irresponsible disposal of waste products to a point where serious public concern is now evident. This has become particularly acute where passive low level exposure to deleterious materials over long periods in the normal living and working environments is suspected. The ultimate effect this may have on health remains very difficult to assess.

The reasons for this are numerous, but two areas provide an insight. Firstly, medical and toxicological research. Toxicological research provides early indication of the possible health effects of new materials but the relationship of such work to true environmental conditions is extremely difficult to interpret. Epidemiological research must of necessity lag behind material developments which inevitably means that the population's health may be at risk in the intervening period. Furthermore, this research is usually based upon workplace experience where exposure levels are generally higher than in the general environment. It is also difficult to separate the effects of a suspected material from the influence of a range of other environmental factors.

The second area involves the practical assessment of the applications within buildings. Here the difficulty is in assessing the dose or exposure an individual might receive. Figure 1.1 lists the interrelated factors affecting dose or exposure which illustrates the problem quite vividly.

Figure 1.1 Factors influencing dose or exposure

Factor	Comments
Form and condition of material	Is the material loose and friable — will it be a source of dust?
	Does it contain volatile elements — will it emit toxic fumes?
	Is it combustible — again will it emit toxic fumes?
	Does it contain naturally radioactive elements?
	What is the concentration of naturally radioactive materials?
Position within the building	Contact with the water supply?
	Contact with food-stuffs?
	Internal or external?
	Exposed or concealed?
	Is there danger from physical contact?
Means of degradation	Abrasion — normal weathering / — normal wear and tear / — DIY activities (sanding)
	Chemical action — corrosion / — drying / — gas emission / — DIY (burning off)
Ventilation	Air change rate — residual properties of dwelling / — normal rates achieved by occupants by opening windows etc.
Lifestyle	Periods of occupation?
	The time factor governing the period of exposure
Maintenance cycles	May introduce toxic chemicals or increase dust in home resulting from maintenance

From these points the magnitude of the task facing the authors may be appreciated. Clearly no one individual could possess the interdisciplinary expertise to develop these ideas to a logical conclusion, hence the necessity of a team of specialists covering the fields of building design and production, environmental science, health and safety, medicine, occupational medicine and toxicology. The structure of the guide stems from the need for such a team of contributors. It is of some significance that a learning process had to be gone through as obviously, with such a group of people from diverse backgrounds, difficulties arose in understanding the terminology used in each other's field and consequently in co-ordination. The editors hope that their attempts at co-ordination have met with some success.

While a review of the health effects of *all* materials available for use in *all* building applications forms a desirable but unrealistic objective clearly some compromise had to be accepted to retain the scope of study within reasonable time and resource constraints.

The study therefore has been directed towards low-rise residential premises, the reasoning being that this forms a large percentage of all buildings both old and new and at the same time is a clearly identifiable area of building technology. Further, it has implications for all sectors of society since, to all intents and purposes, we all live in houses or flats with over sixty percent being owner occupiers.

It has also been necessary to rely upon the current 'state of the art' i.e. to base the study upon current knowledge. The authors have not commissioned any special research and with one or two exceptions no special testing has been undertaken. So in the majority of cases reliance has been put upon general knowledge of the constituents of building materials and upon information supplied by manufacturers regarding their individual formulations.

In considering the overall objective it became obvious that a number of questions would need to be resolved:

1. Which deleterious materials are known or are suspected and why are we concerned about their use in buildings?
2. Where do these materials find application in domestic buildings?
3. What alternatives are available for each application?
4. What are the comparative health hazards of all the alternatives?
5. Will the technical performance and appearance of the alternatives be adequate?
6. What are the comparative costs?
7. What action should be taken when a deleterious material is discovered in an existing building?

It should be noted that, in attempting to provide answers to the questions above, the study has developed from consideration of the known and suspected deleterious materials and the range of possible replacements or substitutes. It is not intended to review *all* the materials available for use in domestic buildings. We have also restricted ourselves to the materials that form part of the building fabric, services and fittings. Furnishings and loose furniture would require a separate study.

While questions 2 and 3 above are relatively easy to resolve, questions 4, 5, 6 and 7 are the most pertinent for the designer. Final selection will require him or her to make health, cost and technical comparisons between the alternatives.

1.1 Health Hazard Assessment

If the building designer is to select appropriate materials to reduce hazards to health and in order to answer question 4 above it is necessary to make a sensible comparative assessment of the main deleterious materials and the substitutes. Thus hazard assessment forms the crux issue and a great deal of the authors' time was devoted to establishing a workable system, because without this, the study could not proceed satisfactorily. The major debate initially was to determine whether an absolute or relative scale of hazard would be most appropriate.

An absolute scale would be ideal but it became obvious that this would be impractical for two main reasons. Firstly, the lack of complete and conclusive toxicological and medical evidence on many of the materials was such that subjective judgements, or at the very least extrapolation from applications in other industries, or from occupational requirements would be necessary. Secondly, the matter was further confused by the need to take into account the position of the material in the building and to relate this to other factors such as the rate of ventilation, in order to estimate the possible 'dose' or exposure to the hazardous material. The problems of achieving this with any degree of confidence have already been identified: see figure 1.1. It is extremely difficult to establish the risk on any absolute basis, without undertaking exhaustive tests and trials.

It was clearly seen that a relative scale was unavoidable and eventually the following system proposed by Dr M. Greenberg was adopted:

A hazard scale of 0–3, identified as

    0 – none reasonably foreseeable
    1 – slight/not yet qualified by research
    2 – moderate
    3 – unacceptable

This scale to be applied to three different categories:

(A)   The potential health hazard to the occupant when the material is in position in the building.
(B)   The potential health hazard to the occupant when a reasonably forseeable disturbance of the material could occur due to maintenance, repair, replacement or fire.
(C)   The long-term potential environmental impact from maintenance, repair, replacement, fire and incorrect waste disposal.

So, for example; asbestos bitumen felt on the A/B/C scale would rate 0/3/3. Zero: due to the fact that when it is fixed in the flat roof of a building the asbestos fibres are encapsulated in bitumen and safe, Three: because the risk of release during maintenance or fire is unacceptable, Three: for the unacceptable long term potential environmental impact due to incorrect waste disposal. On the other hand asbestos vinyl tiles would attract a 2/3/3 rating due to a moderate hazard to the occupant through wear and tear and release of fibres and an unacceptable hazard in the latter two categories.

While this provides a workable system it should not be forgotten that very few normal activities are totally devoid of risk to health. Allergic reactions in susceptible individuals such as hay-fever or from certain types of food are well known. Perhaps less well-known are those risks which are associated with more serious disease and a good example of this is cancer. Such everyday processes as frying or grilling food produce traces of materials which in sufficient amounts have been shown to cause cancer. There is at present controversy whether these very small quantities are completely without risk; at present it is assumed that they are not, although it is agreed that the risk is extremely small. Similarly some materials used in buildings have also been shown to produce cancer under certain conditions. In assessing the safety in use of these materials the authors had to make a judgement whether the risk from the intended use was significantly greater than that normally encountered in everyday life; if in their judgement it was not then it was scored 'none reasonably foreseeable'. However, because many people would prefer to avoid this particular risk, even though it is very small, where it occurs its existence has been recorded.

The problem of the type and nature of the health information available has already been mentioned. As there are insufficient toxiological and medical data available on many of the materials currently in regular use and in particular the recent substitutes for materials such as asbestos fibre, this often means that clear-cut advice cannot be given, so the authors have taken a possibly optimistic view in using factor 1 on the risk assessment scale for materials where the risk is still not determined. However, to penalize a material which may prove perfectly safe causes an equal dilemma.

The authors accept that the use of these somewhat subjective judgements in coming to conclusions is not completely satisfactory, but no doubt as more scientific evidence becomes available a more objective system may develop.

If the risk of a fire involving a material in a given situation has been significantly modified by the choice of an alternative material, then this itself will obviously have an influence on the overall risk to the health of the occupant associated with the choice of material, particularly if there is some significant health hazard associated with the degradation of the material by fire. This has been taken account of in the risk assessment when deciding on the hazard rating for categories B and C of the risk assessment.

Similarly ventilation has also been considered where appropriate and, like fire considerations, is not simply a problem of materials selection but is also influenced by the general building design and layout. However, low rates of ventilation can in themselves be a health hazard so it is important to appreciate the interaction between a possible pollutant and the normal ventilation expected in buildings.

1.2 Ventilation

1.2.1 Ventilation requirements

Ventilation is only one of several methods of controlling indoor, airborne pollutants. Others, primarily based upon source control, include substitution, removal and sealing. Choice in any given circumstance will depend upon the source, the nature of the pollutant, its effects and cost. Control by ventilation is usually achieved by diluting the pollutant to a required concentration using either notionally, pollutant-free outside air, or recirculated air which has been passed through some form of filtration. However, in some cases, where the source of pollutant is well defined, local extraction before the pollutant can mix with the bulk of the air within the space may be preferable. Simple domestic examples include the fireplace and flue, and the cooker hood. Some fresh air will be required in order to replace that which is extracted, in order to ensure satisfactory operation of the extract system.

Ventilation is most appropriate for common pollutants, usually generated by the presence of, or activities associated with, occupants. Examples of these include water vapour, generated by breathing and domestic activities, combustion products, body odours and the products of tobacco smoking. The broad principles of setting ventilation requirements are set out in the Building Research Establishment Digest (B.R.E.) 206. These may be summarized as follows:

(a) Identification of the pollutant(s) of importance, in a given situation.
(b) Specification of the limiting concentration of the pollutant in air.
(c) Estimation of the probable production rates.

Taking (b) and (c) together enables, in principle, a required air supply rate to be derived. In the case of odours, which present particular difficulties, it is usual to omit step (b) and to determine the required dilution flow rates directly, using subjective methods. In choosing ventilation as a control measure it is important to take into account factors such as cost and practicability. The former are primarily related to the energy consumed in the heating season to raise the temperature of outdoor air to the indoor design temperature, but in a mechanically ventilated building also relate to the capital and running costs of the installation. These factors place an upper limit on air supply requirements. Thus, apart from being based upon commonly expected pollutants, the required air supply rates will be determined from generally expected source strengths and, if found to be excessive, other methods, such as source control, will be more appropriate.

Considerations such as these underlie regulations, codes and professional guides which deal with ventilation. Building regulations for England and Wales include specific reference to air supply for combustion appliances, and generally with adequate ventilation for habitable rooms, by specifying required areas of opening, rather than flow rates. A number of British Standard Codes of Practice, relate to fresh air supply and ventilation requirements. The main professional guide, in the UK, is that of the Chartered Institution of Building Services. This sets out both general requirements in relation to the supply of fresh air and includes specific applications to particular types of building, mainly commercial and industrial. There is no specific ventilation requirement for dwellings, but, based mainly upon the need to limit condensation, a minimum whole house ventilation rate in the range 0.5 to 1.0 a.c.h. appears to be appropriate.

From the above, it will be apparent that ventilation is not generally a suitable method for controlling most of the possible airborne pollutants discussed in the following chapters. However, the fresh air requirements quoted provide a basis from which to work when estimating hazards from any contaminants which are liberated into the air from building materials.

1.2.2 Methods of ventilation

It was noted earlier that ventilation may act by dilution or by direct extraction close to the source of the pollutant. In either case this may be achieved either by natural or mechanical means.

Natural ventilation relies upon air flow generated through the building and its envelope by the wind or by the 'stack' effect. The latter results from a difference in air temperature for instance between the air in a building and that outside, or, in the case of a flue, between the hot combustion products and outside air. The general principles of natural ventilation are set out in B.R.E. Digest 210. Mechanical ventilation is self explanatory, but ranges from the simple extractor fan, commonly found in kitchens, to complex ducted systems forming part of a full air-conditioning system in a large building.

The major advantage of mechanical ventilation is that in principle any required flow rate can be supplied to any given location over any prescribed period of time. Control of natural ventilation is limited to the setting of variable openings, such as windows or small 'trickle' ventilators. This lack of control is, however, offset by the relative low cost, both capital and recurrent, of natural ventilation. An additional advantage is the range in ventilation rate achievable with openable windows.

Infiltration is natural ventilation through adventitious openings in the building envelope. These openings include those which can be identified, such as the cracks around the opening lights of windows, but also include often quite complex flow paths, which may not be obvious, particularly at the junctions of components. Infiltration contributes to the air supply within a building, but because it is uncontrollable is often regarded as undesirable, particularly in mechanically ventilated and air-conditioned buildings. In dwellings, however, particularly with the trend away from purpose-provided openings, such as air-bricks, it is often the predominant means of ventilation in winter. Draught-stripping and the sealing of buildings should, therefore, either be done circumspectly, or supplemented with other means, such as mechanical ventilation, to ensure that the basic requirements discussed earlier are satisfied.

1.2.3 Natural ventilation in practice

An indication of the general magnitude of infiltration rates in post-war British housing is provided by a survey reported by Warren and Webb[2]. This gives the results of tracer gas decay measurements, made in 26 houses, over a range of weather conditions where the mean and median infiltration rates were 0.7 a.c.h. and 0.6 a.c.h. respectively. These values are broadly in line with the minimum ventilation requirement range of 0.5 to 1.0 a.c.h. suggested earlier. These values may be compared with results from comparable measurements made on houses in a country such as Sweden with a much colder climate where mean and median values of 0.16 and 0.14, respectively, were found.

The infiltration rate represents the minimum ventilation rate available. However, a number of surveys [3, 5, 6] have shown that, even during the heating season, this is likely to be supplemented by the use of openable windows. Unfortunately there are insufficient data, at present, to estimate the quantitative effect of window opening behaviour on mean ventilation rates, although it has been shown that even relatively limited window opening can give rise to ventilation rates several times the infiltration rate[7].

At present it is reasonable to expect that, on average, ventilation rates experienced in UK housing will broadly be in line with the need to control condensation and other common pollutants and, provided the appropriate regulations are followed, to provide air for combustion appliances. However, as the results described above attest, it is possible, either by changes in design and construction technique in new housing, or by retrofit measures in existing housing, to substantially increase air-tightness with a consequent reduction in infiltration rates.

The long-term effect of the possible reduced infiltration rates on the health of the occupant is not, as yet, fully understood.

1.3 Technical and aesthetic assessment

Initially it was thought that the technical performance and the aesthetic merit of materials would need to be separated but in reality most of the applications are such that aesthetic considerations have not proved to be of great importance in selection, so the two factors are combined where appropriate.

For each application the materials have been compared against a performance specification which may exceed the minimum laid down in Building Regulations but generally is related to normal building design and construction practice.

The assessment used for technical and aesthetic performance is relative on a scale of 1–10. A simpler scale is adopted as the problems associated with investigating the comparative performance are less severe, as this type of technical comparison is commonly carried out by designers. This scale is provided to assist but it is anticipated that it does not cover every conceivable usage of the materials. Designers must therefore exercise their own judgement in individual circumstances.

On the 1–10 scale, 1 represents the best material available, i.e. that considered to be most suitable from a technical point of view, and 10 to be generally unsuitable for the application under consideration or having a poor life expectancy. In all cases the grading is a compromise considering all function and performance factors, durability and buildability, i.e. the ease of construction. It could be argued that the latter factor is of lesser importance but this does affect the contractor's perception of the best material to use.

1.4 Building costs

Estimated building costs have been provided for each material application. These are the costs actually incurred by the builder in the normal course of his business and are current at January, 1985 for work in the Outer London area.

To enable a cost comparison to be made each material application has been described and, where appropriate, dimensions given. Costs have been expressed on a unit basis and as a total cost per dwelling. The dwelling on which total costs are based is shown in Figure 1.2.

The building costs reflect the pricing level you would expect when constructing a single dwelling of moderate size. It must be remembered that the following factors will have a significant effect on building costs:

1.   Quantity
2.   Locality of the site
3.   Discounts offered by suppliers

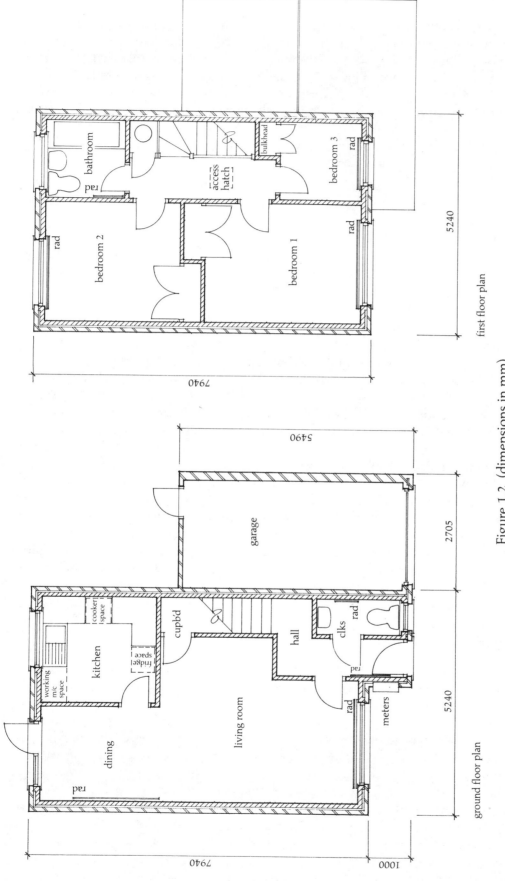

Figure 1.2 (dimensions in mm)

1.5 Use of the guide

In an effort to provide precise and useful information for those involved in the design process the detailed results of the health, technical and cost comparisons for individual applications are shown in a concise, data sheet format in Section III. Each sheet also provides overall guidance on selection for new buildings as well as comments upon the possible problems encountered with each application in existing buildings. Detailed guidance upon the use of the data sheets is provided in the introduction to Section III.

However, designers and specifiers should resist the temptation to rely solely upon Section III. In order to appreciate the detailed health risk assessment findings on the data sheets it is necessary to have a broad understanding of Section II, which consists of a review of the recognized health hazards posed by building materials. The importance of this general understanding cannot be overstated, and although architects and other designers may feel that this is another imposition on their already short design time, and perhaps even on their design freedom, it has become obvious that these issues must be given more consideration as subsequent expensive remedial or removal measures resulting from unwise selection may ultimately result in claims for negligence.

1.6 Future considerations

In the preceding comments a number of questions have been raised to which it is hoped the following sections will go some way to provide the answers. However, we must also be aware that we might be jumping from the 'frying pan into the fire' when specifying new, relatively untried alternative materials. Research continues, often not at the pace it should, so that in the future today's assessments may require modification as new evidence is revealed. It is essential that we continue to be vigilant; the necessary questions must be asked and appropriate research and testing instigated.

In connection with this it is important that the briefs of the Agrément Board and British Standards Institution committees for building materials and components are adjusted to include not only the consideration of the health hazards to the building operative but also those to the occupants and users of buildings. It is only recently that BSI committees have been requested to review the use of asbestos fibre in current materials standards and we understand it will take a considerable period to work through all the standards.

This is a step in the right direction but for many it is long overdue.

There are also problems over disclosure of information. While it is appreciated that certain trade secrets on precise contents of manufacturer's products are necessary for commercial reasons, it is alarming to note the reluctance of many manufacturers to declare even the basic materials used in their formulations, without the need to apply extra pressure. On the other hand many manufacturers have been only too willing to co-operate with the authors once they were advised of the objectives of the study. In many cases manufacturers produce excellent guidance for building operatives on the safe use and handling of their products which usually includes fairly precise details of constituents. Architects should take an interest in this information and manufacturers ought to consider supplying an abbreviated version of this type of information with the standard trade literature sent to designers.

Since from time to time manufacturers alter the product composition from that investigated by the study group it is not possible to produce lists of the names of manufacturers whose products comply with the findings, and so it is suggested that, when specifying any product where the health issue is of importance, the manufacturer or supplier be contacted if there is any doubt concerning the contents of the products.

There is also the need to improve educational courses at all levels in the construction industry to include guidance on health hazards. Many designers may initially be very surprised at the number of applications of lead and asbestos we have identified in domestic buildings and may well then receive a further shock when they find that often there are suitable alternatives available at lower cost.

This situation could be overcome by improved technical education so that in future designers are more aware of these issues. Where there is a suitable alternative available, offering lower health hazard, at an acceptable cost, use it!

The final decision will be influenced by the individual's perception of the risks involved and designers must attempt to gauge their client's feelings on these issues. The public perception of risk has been recognized by the Royal Commission on Environmental Pollution in its 10th report[8].

> 'No human activity is without risk, but it is evident that the risks associated with some activities are less acceptable than others. Pollution problems such as those associated with lead, asbestos, the handling and transport of radioactive materials and the use of certain agricultural chemicals, are increasingly being seen by the public to pose risks which are unacceptable, despite the fact that activities with risks which are mathematically at least as great, if not greater, are consider to be more acceptable.'

Public perception of the risk involved in buildings and with building materials is a problem with which the building industry as a whole has to live. Undoubtedly, it will provide an impetus for change in the future.

1.7 References

1.   BS Codes of Practice:
           BS 5720: 1979 — Code of Practice for Mechanical Ventilation and Air-conditioning in Buildings.
           BS 5925: 1980 — Code of Practice for the Design of Buildings: Ventilation Principles and Designing for Natural Ventilation.
           BS 5250: 1975 — Code of Basic Data for the Design of Buildings: The Control of Condensation in dwellings.
           BS 5440: 1976 — Code of Practice for Flues and Air Supply for Gas Appliances of Rated Input not exceeding 60 kW: Air Supply.
2.   Warren, P.R. and Webb, B.C. Ventilation measurements in housing. Proceedings of CIBS Symposium —Natural Ventilation by Design — Garston, 20 October 1980. pp. 22—31.
3.   Kronvall, J. Airtightness — Measurements and Measurement Methods. Swedish Council for Building Research, Report F8: 1980.
4.   Brundrett, G.W. (1977) Ventilation: A Behavioural Approach. *Energy Research,* **Vol.1,** pp. 289—298.
5.   Brundrett, G.W. (1979) Window Ventilation and Human Behaviour. Proceedings of the first International Indoor Climate Symposium, Copenhagen, August 1978. Ed. P.O. Fanger and O. Valbjorn. Danish Building Research Institute.
6.   Dick, J.B. and Thomas, D.A. (1951) Ventilation Research in Occupied Houses. *JIHVE,* **Vol.19,** October, pp. 306—326.
7.   Dickson, D.J. Ventilation with Open Windows. Electricity Council Research Centre Report. ECRC/M1329. April 1980.
8.   Royal Commission on Environmental Pollution, Tenth Report. *Tackling Pollution — Experience and Prospects,* p.16, 1984, London, HMSO.

SECTION II

HAZARDS TO HEALTH FROM BUILDING MATERIALS

2 Asbestos and other natural materials

M. GREENBERG, MB FRCP

2.1 Asbestos

2.1.1 A brief history of asbestos in modern times

From being a historic curiosity, asbestos started its career as an important commercial material in the 1860s, initially in small tonnage with limited specialized applications. By 1898 HM Women Inspectors of Factories reported their observations that work with asbestos was an easily demonstrable cause of danger to the health of workers, with injury to bronchial tubes and lungs medically attributed to their employment. In 1899 Montague Murray had referred to him a man of 33 with severe pulmonary fibrosis, not due to tuberculosis, who had started work with asbestos at the age of 19. Although he died the following year the case was not reported until 1907. Of interest is that the patient told Dr Murray that of the 10 people with whom he started work he was the only survivor, the others having died by the age of 30. Subsequently further cases were recognized in various parts of the world and by 1930 asbestosis had arrived. Sporadic cases of associated lung cancer (bronchial carcinoma) appeared from 1935 onwards until finally it was agreed to be caused by asbestos though not without controversy. Similarly, a rare tumour of the lining of the chest (malignant mesothelioma) was reported from time to time in asbestos workers and was only 'recognized' in the early 1960s. A similar tumour of the lining of the abdomen (peritoneal mesothelioma) was also found to excess in association with asbestos exposure.

Although the major interest was focused on workers engaged on asbestos work, in due course workers downwind were found to share disease, and members of the households of asbestos workers were found to develop disease from dust brought home on clothing. Disease was also discovered in people living in the vicinity of asbestos mines and factories, and in people living in districts where the soil was rich in fibre.

Studies of the environment in special situations, water supplies, food-stuffs and pharmaceuticals revealed how widespread fibre contamination was and gave rise to concern about the possible hazard to the general population. A number of studies have attempted to evaluate the environmental impact of asbestos with conflicting results. As a generalization it can be said that unless the effects were substantial, epidemiological methods are too insensitive to detect orders of hazard that might be unacceptable to the general public (historically a hazard has been 'acceptable' to workers if an excess mortality of 2% has not been exceeded). In the absence of adequate data prudence has counselled that exposure should be as low as is reasonably practicable.

2.1.2 Asbestos in buildings

In old housing stock all three types of asbestos may be found.

1. *White* (chrysotile) may be found incorporated with other materials in board or sheeting in various concentrations, or in surface treatments, or as insulation (thermal and/or acoustic), or in pipes.
2. *Brown* (amosite = trade name for asbestiform cummingtonite — grunerite) may be found incorporated in laminated boards as well as in pipe insulation.
3. *Blue* (crocidolite) may be found in more or less pure form as fire insulation on steel frames or thermal insulation to heating systems. It may also be found mixed with other forms of asbestos in board or in asbestos cement mixed with chrysotile.

Contemporary building materials currently manufactured in the UK when they use asbestos do so in the form of chrysotile. Amosite and crocidolite may however be incorporated in imported materials and be found in older materials. Both are used without restriction in certain European countries and the impending EEC Directives on worker protection and consumer products, may not proscribe them. A voluntary labelling scheme has been in operation for some time and a compulsory labelling scheme features in the Community Asbestos marketing directive. However, it is to be expected that after a period *in situ* the identification of materials may become obscured.

British Standards (BSI) exist for a number of products incorporating asbestos: currently through its committee systems the British Standards Institution is embarking on a review programme to consider health aspects and the feasibility of substitution.

2.1.3 The effects of asbestos on health

(a) *Asbestosis*

In this condition the normal structure of that part of the lung that is concerned with the uptake of oxygen and the discharge of carbon dioxide from the blood is altered so that not only is this important function disturbed but extra work has to be done in operating a lung that has lost its ready expansion and elasticity. Distortion produced by scar tissue also impairs the ready flow of air in the tubes. A dose response relationship exists for this condition and a threshold of effect can be derived. It is not reasonably foreseeable that this condition is a risk to occupiers in any of their activities (see Advisory Committee on Asbestos Report 1979 and Acheson and Gardner, 1983).

(b) *Lung cancer (carcinoma of the bronchus)*

This is the common cancer that is associated with cigarette smoking and other environmental agents. While it is a hazard of non-smokers working with asbestos, the hazard is considerably enhanced by cigarette smoking. A dose response has been derived for this condition but as no threshold has been identified, i.e. a level below which it is certain that no hazard exists, wherever asbestos fibres occur in the atmosphere a lung cancer potential is thought to exist. At the low levels of environmental contamination that commonly obtain in buildings containing asbestos, or the relatively short term and lowish levels that may result from repair and maintenance, the order of hazard is low but finite for the DIY occupier; it may however be substantial for the specialist builder/decorator/plumber/electrician/heating engineer, unless precautionary measures are adopted that are not common practice for them.

(c) *Malignant mesothelioma of peritoneum or pleura*

A rare and as yet incurable tumour of the linings of the chest and the surface of the intestines. Currently some 500 cases are notified a year in the UK: it is considered that a majority have an ascertainable asbestos exposure history.

The dose response relationship is qualitative. While prolonged heavy exposures to asbestos are commonly an associated feature, brief exposures which may be heavy are also associated with tumours usually several decades after the event. No threshold has been determined.

(d) *Other tumours*

In addition to these conditions, other tumours have been found to occur to excess in studies of exposed workers. Of these, carcinoma of the larynx has the strongest association: gastro-intestinal cancer and other cancers may also be causally associated.

(e) *Non-malignant pleural disease*

Other causally associated conditions found in workers and their families involve thickening and hardening of the outer surface of the lung (pleural plaques, pleural thickening calcification)

2.1.4 Relative risk of fibre types

The league table for harmfulness of asbestos types is customarily given as crocidolite> amosite>chrysotile. This seems to apply to malignant mesothelioma but the order of harmfulness may be less markedly different with respect to lung cancer and asbestosis. The relative harmfulness may be less an intrinsic property of the mineral but rather the propensity to break up into fine, more hazardous, fibre.

(a) *Acceptable hazard*
Published hygiene standards for asbestos relate to workers. They are levels that can be achieved in the current state of technology. Though they are associated with a level of excess mortality that can be estimated, they have been accepted for now following negotiation between representatives of interested parties. There is an overriding requirement however that the exposure should be necessary and that such exposure be as low as is reasonably practicable. An acceptable exposure level in the non-occupational field cannot be derived from the current hygiene standard: the practice of 'adjusting' from a 40 hour week to a 168 hour week and then dividing by 10 has no sanction.

The current widely accepted philosophy of asbestos use is based on a series of value judgements; its use must be considered essential on the basis of economy, technical properties and safety.

Ideally, asbestos products should have the fibre firmly bound at the start of its life, should require no maintenance to preserve this property and should not be involved in applications that necessitate it being cut, drilled or ground on site. So that fibre is not released it should not be subject to injury or attrition in reasonably foreseeable use. Because it may not be readily identifiable after being installed for some period, if it is considered essential to install asbestos material, then the concerned builder might consider the provision of a handbook with a guide to its position, maintenance where desirable and safe disposal.

2.1.5 Waste disposal

The removal or disposal of asbestos materials presents a potential hazard if fibres are released. Unless these operations are carried out expertly not only may the remover be at hazard but also those in the immediate environs may be at risk. The extent to which a community environmental risk may occur and the timescale will depend on disposal methods and the nature of the asbestos.

2.1.6 Uses of asbestos in domestic buildings

(a) *Asbestos in cement matrix (asbestos cement)*
As currently produced in the UK the fibre in roofing and cladding sheets will be chrysotile. The cement 'binding' can be broken down by hand or power tools, injury, attrition, weathering or by 'aggressive' water leading to direct or indirect environmental contamination. Once installed in a building, the hazard to the occupier of say asbestos cement sheeting will depend on the likelihood and extent of wear and exposure in its normal position and in any subsequent maintenance and renovation.

The fibre in pipe and water tanks produced in the UK is chrysotile. Old products may include other forms of asbestos.

External pipes, even if alterations are not made to the plumbing that involve cutting or refixing and fibre release, may become discoloured and be subjected to wire brushing and fibre release.

Fibre leaches from asbestos cement in contact with water: the rate varies as the aggressivity of the water (which relates to pH and ion content). The inhalation of fibre is unequivocally a potential hazard. It is assumed that the fraction that is subsequently cleared in mucus and swallowed is of no account. There is however considerable controversy concerning the subsequent fate of swallowed fibres and their significance, both for individuals at work and for the population exposed to asbestos in food and drink.

(b) *Asbestos in polymermatrix*

Asbestos has found a use as a filler and stabilizer, as well as an ingredient in backing material of vinyl floor sheeting and tiles.

Attrition of floor surfaces may release fibre as will ripping up worn flooring which may lead to contamination of the building. Fine fibre particles will be disseminated by cleaning, movement and convection. Concern has been expressed for infants who live at floor level but arguably it is their infancy that predisposes them to enhanced hazard.

It is very difficult to mark these products so that they can be readily identified at the time of disposal.

Pyrolysis will generate irritant fume and release fibre: if the temperature is high enough chrysotile will be altered to a less toxic mineral.

(c) *Asbestos in bitumen matrix*

Normally used as roofing felts and in the normal intact form, fibre is firmly bound. In situ it presents no hazard to the occupier. Over time this material may embrittle: subsequent replacement will involve a hazard predominantly to the roofer: only the most intrepid DIY practitioner will attempt loft alteration. Dumping the discarded material in the usual manner (assuming it is no longer identifiable) will present a small environmental hazard for a time. In the event of fire, products of pyrolysis will not be a substantial hazard though there may be fibre release.

(d) *Asbestos paint*

In the day-to-day life of the building this will present no hazard. Over time resins break down and some fibre release may occur. Repainting, however, if it involves rubbing down, will release fibre. Heat or chemical stripping may delay the potential fibre release. Even when asbestos is omitted from new products, the hazard may still be present from old applications.

2.2 Timber

While various wood dusts have a range of toxic, immunological and carcinogenic properties, installed and in the lump timber presents no problems for health. Associated hazards to occupiers however will result from products of pyrolysis, wood preservatives and surface treatments, fungal contamination and adhesives.

The irritant, asphyxiant and toxic fumes of this natural polymer are as hazardous as many a synthetic: they constitute the major hazard of household fires.

Wood preservatives are increasingly being suspected as having carcinogenic properties. Underfloor timbers after treatment may continue to give off vapour. If the floor is permeable, the rooms above become contaminated. Untreated wood in damp, poorly ventilated conditions is susceptible to dry rot, the spores of which may be responsible for bronchial asthma if they enter the household environment.

Ply, block and compound boards may, if not up to specification, emit breakdown products or unreacted components of their resin binders.

Current awareness is of formaldehyde. Although in the UK the major focus has been on cavity wall installation, in the USA attention has been drawn to build-up from boards in reduced ventilation/fuel efficiency buildings. The evidence for carcinogenicity of formaldehyde is based on animal study. There is no definitive evidence to confirm this effect on man nor to rebut it: both positive and negative studies have been reported which merit further investigation. However, on the basis of amenity, appreciable levels of formaldehyde are to be eschewed and, on the basis of prudence, environmental levels should be well controlled.

2.3 Cellulose fibre

Adequate toxicity testing appears not to have been carried out on this material: human exposure has been short in general and the study of substantial populations has not been carried out. If particle size distribution indicates that a substantial proportion is in the non-inhalable range, then as far as the lower respiratory tract and lungs are concerned, there is unlikely to be a problem. If particles include sizes that may settle out in the nasal passages, then, extrapolating from wood dust experience, thought should be given to the possibility that the installer, who in this case might well be the occupier, may be at risk from nasal disease.

Pyrolysis presents the same problems as for wood, though the fire suppressant may reduce the hazard. The addition of fungicides and pesticides will present toxicity problems if fibres are not contained.

2.4 Calcium silicate board

The term calcium silicate covers a range of chemical compounds, natural and semi-synthetic, some of which have 'fibre' forms. The boards have included mixed mineral fibre: the trend has been to omit asbestos and either to replace with other fibres or simply to omit addition. Board either without fibre inclusion or with fibres that have diameters greater than 5 microns can be considered to be of low hazard when comminuted, by wear or cutting.

Pyrolysis presents no special hazard.

2.5 Mineral fibre

The term normally excludes asbestos but includes a range of natural and man-made mineral fibres. This is given detailed consideration elsewhere (see Section 2.2).

2.6 Vermiculite

Vermiculite granules have been considered as nuisance dust; however, studies of samples of mineral have on occasion been shown to include asbestos fibre as well as 'fibrous' vermiculite. Interim human studies have suggested a lung cancer hazard — these require to be confirmed. In the interim, non-fibrous vermiculite should be specified for domestic insulation. Loose fill in lofts can insinuate itself into the upper storey.

2.7 Natural slate

No foreseeable hazard for occupants.

2.8 Concrete slate

No foreseeable risk of disease for occupants.

2.9 Phosphogypsum*

Plasterboard, employed as a wall or ceiling lining, may be manufactured using phosphogypsum.

Some finite level of radioactivity may be detected in any natural building material. Concern with phosphogypsum in wallboards arises simply because the level of radium-226 is over thirty times higher than in natural gypsum.

Radium-226 undergoes radioactive (alpha) decay to form the gaseous radon-222 which, in turn, generates a series of radioactive products or 'daughters'. It is the decay of these short-lived radon daughters which poses the main radiological risk to health.

Radon within a dwelling may arise from three main sources: it emanates from the materials used in the building fabric; it enters with the air which ventilates the building; it enters from the ground beneath the dwelling. On average the total amount entering the building is 50% via the ground, 25% through ventilation and 25% from the building fabric. In some parts of the country the amount coming from the ground will be a higher percentage. Thus it can be seen that even a total eradication of radioactivity from building materials would entail no more than a 25% decline in the radon-related daughters.

The damage to health (denoted by '1 dose equivalent'[2]) may result from the exposure of the whole body to gamma rays (similar to X-rays) emitted by the radon daughters in the air or the wallboards. In addition, internal radiation damage to lung tissue results from the radioactive decay of daughter products inhaled as particles suspended in the air within the building.

It has been calculated[1] that, for a typical two storey, three bedroom, centre terrace house with 270 m² of 12.7 mm thick plasterboard containing phosphogypsum, the additional annual dose from gamma exposure amounts to 0.15 milliSieverts Hand the additional dose due to inhalation of the daughter products is, assuming one air change per hour, 0.05 mSv; therefore, the annual dose equivalent increases by only 0.20 mSv compared with that in a house lined with natural gypsum wallboards.

To put this in perspective, this figure is equivalent to about 10% increase in the dose normally received from all sources of natural radiation. The contribution from radon from phosphogypsum wallboard is equivalent to about a 14% increase in the dose normally received from radon. The latter is about a third of the total dose from all sources, both natural and artificial in origin, that people are subjected to in their normal lives. So it can be seen that the additional radiation dose and hence risk from phosphogypsum plaster is small.

2.10 Bibliography

Selikoff, I.J. and Lee, D.H.K. (1978) *Asbestos and Disease*, Academic Press.

Asbestos: final report of the Advisory Committee (1979) Vols 1 and 2, HMSO, London.

Acheson, E.D. and Gardner, M.J. (1983) *The control limit for asbestos*, HMSO, London.

Biological effects of man-made mineral-fibre, Report of WHO/IARC meeting, Euro Reports and Studies 81, WHO, Copenhagen 1983.

Parkes, W.R. (1982) *Occupational lung disorder*, Butterworths 2nd Edition 1982.

A guide to the Asbestos (licensing) Regulations 1983, Health and Safety Series booklet HS(R) 19, HMSO, London.

Wrixon, A.D. and O'Riordan, M.C. (1980). Radiological Criteria for the Use of Phosphogypsum as a Building Material, Proceedings of International Symposium on Phosphogypsum, Florida, 5th–7th November 1980.

Recommendations of the International Commission on Radiological Protection, ICRP Publication No 26 (1977)

Principles for limiting exposure of the public to natural sources of radiation, Oxford, Pergamon Press, ICRP Publication 39. Am ICRP, 14 No 1 (1984).

* Section 2.9 contributed by Dr C.E. Miller

3 Man-made mineral fibres

J. DODGSON, Bsc DipEd FIOH

3.1 Introduction

A wide range of mineral fibres are now available for use in the building and construction industries. These comprise:

1. Man-made mineral fibres (MMMF), a generic term used to describe the amorphous glassy fibres made from molten blast-furnace slag or other readily fusible slags, natural rocks and minerals, basalt, diabase, olivine, and borosilicate or calcium aluminium silicate glass. These are frequently referred to collectively as 'mineral wools'.
2. Ceramic fibres, another form of MMF, produced from aluminium silicate minerals such as kaolin. These are generally amorphous but some reconversion to crystalline form can occur at high temperatures.
3. Synthetic mineral fibres, usually crytalline, including fibres produced from alumina, graphite, potassium titanate, silicas and zirconia.
4. Naturally occuring fibres which are generally crystalline. These include the asbestos minerals — chrysotile, amosite, crocidolite, tremolite and anthophyllite — and others such as attapulgite, sepiolite, wollastonite and zeolites (see Section 2.1).

3.2 Physical and chemical properties of fibres

The physical and chemical properties of these fibres differ considerably, for example, in terms of their physical strength, temperature resistance, insulation properties, physical size and solubility in acid or alkali media. These differences largely determine their industrial uses, together with considerations of manufacturing costs and availability. The ceramic fibres and refractory synthetic mineral fibres are mainly used for high temperature applications in industrial plants or other specialized industrial situations and are not considered here. This section deals with the use of MMMF materials only.

3.3 A brief history of MMMF

Production of MMMF products has increased considerably over the last 20 years to meet the needs of energy conservation, better insulation and structural reinforcement. In addition, these materials have been widely used as a potentially safe substitute for asbestos. However, experimental work[1,2] involving the implantation of glass and other natural and synthetic fibres in the pleural or peritoneal cavities of animals led to development of tumours similar to mesothelioma caused in man by asbestos. This work was originally designed to show how asbestos fibres might produce their carcinogenic effect. Its conclusion was that carcinogenicity was more closely related to the physical size of the fibres (morphology) than to differences in mineralogical composition. Fibres of length greater than 8 microns and diameter of less than 0.25 microns were the most carcinogenic. These studies attracted interest in the possible health hazards of inhaling respirable fibres from MMMF materials (that is, the fine fibres that can penetrate to and deposit in the lungs) and stimulated extensive research on the long-term risks to health in the manufacture and use of MMMF products. This review aims to assess the present evidence on potential health risks in relation to the use of MMMF in building materials, especially those used in domestic buildings.

3.4 Types of MMMF

There are three main types of MMMF:

1.   Continuous filament glass fibres;
2.   Insulation wools;
3.   Special purpose fibres.

3.4.1 Continuous filament glass fibres

Continuous filament glass fibres are produced to a pre-determined diameter by mechanically drawing extruded threads of molten glass through a small orifice of defined size. These long filaments are usually made in relatively large diameters ranging from about 6 to 25 microns but with a very narrow size distribution about the selected size. For this reason few respirable fibres (i.e. those of less than 3 microns diameter which can penetrate to the lungs) occur with continuous filament glass fibres.

3.4.2 Insulation wools

Insulation wools (or mineral wools) are made from slag, rock or glass by a combination of blowing and spinning processes to fiberize the melts. In the USA the term mineral wool is often used to describe mixtures of slag and rockwool only. The processes used for insulation wools produce a range of fibres of different lengths and diameter together with unfiberized particles of similar mineral composition formed from solidified droplets.

Manufacturers characterize their MMMF products by their 'nominal diameter' — a length weighted measure of mean fibre diameter. The nominal diameter of insulation wools being manufactured now is about 6 microns. However, the fibre diameter distribution in these materials is rather broad and a substantial proportion of the fibres present are less than 3 microns in diameter. The nominal diameters of older insulation wools, especially glasswools, were much higher (15 — 30 microns). Recent research has shown that substantial proportions of fine fibres (less than 3 microns diameter) were still present in these older products. Technical developments in production to improve insulation properties of the wools reduced the proportion of coarse fibres. Present production material is close to the optimum size (4—6 microns) for insulation purposes and further major changes in fibre size are unlikely.

3.4.3 Special purpose fibres

Special purpose fibres are made by further attenuation of glass fibres. These fine glass fibres have much smaller diameters than the insulation wools, being in the range 1—3 microns. Some very fine glass fibres (less than 1 micron diameter) are also made.

3.5 Health effects

3.5.1 Areas of concern

Man-made fibres have been produced for more than forty years and the effects on workers' health have been examined intensively. Complaints of skin and eye irritations arising from close contact with MMMF materials are well known, particularly from workers handling MMMF for the first time or after a period of absence from contact. These complaints do not usually persist with continued exposure[3,4] except with a minority of workers. Acute effect of MMMF on eyes have recently been shown to be related to the degree of exposure to MMMF dust and the use of protective eye glasses was recommended.[5]

Substantial exposure to MMMF can result in irritation of the upper respiratory tract though the effects are usually transitory and have not been considered to be a long-term health risk[3,4] at current levels of exposure. The occurrence of respiratory symptoms might be expected to be related to dust exposure but early studies of this relationship were inconclusive.

Nevertheless, the Health and Safety Commission,[4] after reviewing the evidence then available, proposed a UK control limit of 5 mg/m^3 of total dust in air for MMMF workers in recognition of the fact that these respiratory effects implied that MMMF could not be simply treated as a biologically inert dust to which a nuisance dust limit applies (10 mg/m^3). In adddition, a 5 fibres per millilitre control limit for respirable fibres was proposed for MMMF workers to minimize potential carcinogenic risks from respirable fibres suggested in the earlier experimental studies with animals (see Section 2.2.3). The Commission recognized the tentative and subjective nature of these proposals and it considered it important to check the proposals against results of research as they became available. More recently[6] the Health and Safety Executive have published their intention to introduce a 1 fibre per millilitre recommended lim... ror superfine MMMF (i.e. fibres of less than 1 micron diameter). They have subsequently confirmed the introduction of the 5mg/m^3 control limit for MMMF (but *not* the 5 fibre per millilitre limit)[7].

3.5.2 Results of recent research

Large-scale animal, environmental and epidemiological studies into the possible health hazards of MMMF have been funded by the European and American manufacturing industries for almost ten years. The research has been carried out by independent institutes in Europe and the USA and the results were reported in 1982 at a meeting organized by the World Health Organisation in Copenhagen. Research conducted by other groups not involved in the industrial sponsored work was also presented at this meeting. The published proceedings[8] include peer reviews of the results by eminent scientists.

The *environmental surveys* of fibre concentrations in MMMF plants show that current exposure levels were generally low. Mean concentrations of respirable fibres were mainly less than 0.1 fibres/ml in both the American and European studies, though levels exceeding 1 fibre/ml occurred occasionally at processes where the fine special purpose fibres were manufactured. On the other hand mean fibre concentrations at continuous fibre plants were less than 0.02 fibres/ml. These fibre levels are considerably lower than those experienced in the asbestos industry. The airborne MMMF fibres were also substantially thicker and longer than asbestos and the proportion of very fine, potentially, carcinogenic fibres, was very much lower. Mean concentrations of total dust at the MMMF plants were usually around 5 mg/m^3 or less, although some higher mean values occurred. Much of the airborne dust was not fibrous. These environmental data were used in the epidemiological studies. Some evidence was presented which supported the view that past exposure levels may have been substantially higher when MMMF wools were produced without oil or binder. Oil and binder-free MMMF materials were produced at some plants prior to 1960, but nearly all products since then include oil and binder.

The *epidemiological studies* in Europe and the USA included observations on large groups of workers employed in the MMMF industry, over 25,000 in the former case and more than 16,000 in the latter. No excess in overall mortality rate for all causes of death from mesothelioma tumours was found in either study (only one death from mesothelioma was reported) when the results were compared with those for the appropriate general population. Nor was there an overall excess of cancer of the lung. On the other hand both studies showed an excess of lung cancer in small groups of workers 30 years or more after first exposure. There was no association of the increased mortality with either the intensity or duration of the fibre exposure, as would be expected if exposure to fibres was the cause of the increase. It is possible that this increase in mortality may be related to other occupational (e.g. use of asbestos or organic binders) or non-occupational factors (e.g. smoking). Some evidence was presented from a Swedish study of workers in the MMMF user industry which also indicated an increased risk of lung cancer, though confounding factors — especially exposure to asbestos — may be important in this case. Nevertheless, while caution should be exercised in interpreting these results, further clarification of the potential risk of lung cancer is needed.

At the present time, a further follow-up study of the population included in the European epidemiological study is being conducted by the International Agency for Research on Cancer, Lyon. Collaborative studies of possible confounding occupational factors on a retrospective basis are being made by the Institute of Occupational Medicine, Edinburgh, at the MMMF plants concerned. The results of this combined study will be reported towards the end of 1985. These investigations will enable a larger group of MMMF workers to be examined 30 years or more after first exposure and allow an assessment of the possible influence of other factors.

Epidemiological studies of respiratory morbidity among workers in the manufacturing industry were also reported at the conference. Respiratory symptoms and impairment of lung function were not related to past exposure to MMMF, although some small radiographic opacities in the lungs of a limited number of exposed men were reported. There was an absence of corresponding data for the user industry. Further longitudinal epidemiological investigations to clarify the findings were recommended.

Several groups reported animal research studies designed to test the carcinogenic and fibrogenic potential of MMMF when animals were allowed *to inhale* the fibres. This type of exposure mimics that experienced by man more closely than that induced by implantation. The results were compared with those from unexposed animals and animals exposed to asbestos. These investigations supported the hypothesis that MMMF in general production did not cause lung cancer, pulmonary fibrosis or mesothelioma (the tumour in the lining of the lung which is typical of asbestos fibres). The absence of carcinogenic effects was considered consistent with the physical and chemical properties of MMMF: these fibres have larger diameters than airborne asbestos and would be expected to be less carcinogenic; MMMF can only split transversely, thus producing shorter fibres of the same diameter, whereas asbestos splits longitudinally to form finer fibres; MMMF are also more soluble than asbestos. These factors would be expected to assist natural clearance from the lung.

3.5.3 Conclusion

Taken together the results of the detailed researches suggest that exposure to MMMF at the levels currently encountered in the manufacturing industry should not give undue concern, though exposure to MMMF should be minimized as far as is reasonably practicable. Further explanation of the small risk of lung cancer 30 years or more after first exposure is desirable and relevant research is in hand.

3.6 Domestic usage of MMMF materials

Rock and glass wools are commonly used in roll form for loft insulation and in a shredded form for in-filling wall cavities or lofts. The wools may also be compressed into bats or boards for use as partitions or insulation screens or into pipe sections for insulating various pipe diameters. Ceiling and wall tiles are also made by compression. Chopped continuous fibre is also used in reinforced plastics.

The release of fibre from loft insulations can occur when entering or working in the loft and could enter the water system if water tanks in the roof space are not properly covered with a well fitted lid. Contamination of other rooms could occur from fibres released through structural gaps, for example at the inner leaf of the external wall, or through down lighters around pipes from the loft to lower rooms.

Neither cavity wall, timber frame insulation nor compressed sections should release significant amounts of fibre in normal use though care will be needed to minimize exposure during maintenance work.

Loose MMMF insulation around hot and cold water tanks is usually encased in polythene. Alternatively, rigid MMMF compressed boards may be employed. Such tanks are often accessible in airing cupboards and there is a small risk of contaminating clothes if the insulation is not properly encased. Similar insulation is also used around boilers for central heating. Some release of fibres might be expected during maintenance when the casing is removed but not otherwise.

In general, the long-term exposure of occupiers of domestic properties where MMMF materials have been properly installed should be extremely low. On the basis of the above health evidence from industry the general use of MMMF materials in buildings ought not to cause any concern provided sensible precautions are taken to minimize fibre release. Simple protective measures using suitable clothing, gloves, eye glasses or disposable respirators can be utilized during DIY work should skin, eye or respiratory tract irritations occur.

3.7 References

1. Stanton, M.F., Wrench, C. (1972) Mechanism of mesothelioma induction with asbestos and fibrous glass. *J. Nat Cancer Inst.* **48**, 797—821.

2. Stanton, M.F. *et al* (1977) Carcinogenicity of fibrous glass pleural response in relation to fibre diameters. *J. Nat Cancer Inst.* **58**, 3.

3. Hill, J.W. (1976) Health aspects of man-made fibres. A Review *Ann. Occup. Hyg.,* **20**, 2.

4. Health and Safety Commission (1979) Discussion document: Man-made mineral fibres. Report of a working party to the Advisory Committee on Toxic Substances. HMSO, London.

5. Stockholm Jetal (1982) Ophthamologic effects of man-made mineral fibres. *Scandanavian Journal Work Environmental Health,* **8**, 185—190.

6. Health & Safety Executive (1984). Toxic Substances Bulletin, December 1984.

7. World Health Organisation (1983) Biological effects of man-made mineral fibres. Report on a WHO/IARC meeting in Copenhagen 20th—22nd April 1982. In: EURO Reports and Studies 81. Pub: WHO Copenhagen.

4 Metals

R.M. HARRISON, PhD

4.1 Introduction

Metals find many applications in building. In most instances they are quite innocuous, although in some cases they do give cause for concern. The metals most widely used in house building are: aluminium, plain and galvanized (i.e. zinc coated) iron or steel, stainless steel, copper and lead. Other metals (e.g. chromium) are components of paints and also require consideration.

4.2 Toxicology

4.2.1 Aluminium

Aluminium is an abundant element in the natural environment. Normal adult daily intake is within the range 10–100 milligrams and is without known adverse effect. The main route of intake is dietary, and absorption via the gastrointestinal tract (stomach and gut) is very inefficient. Bypass of this barrier, either by industrial exposure to bauxite fume (small airborne particles of aluminium oxide) or through kidney dialysis with non-deionized aluminium-coagulated tapwater can lead to serious toxic effects.

In normal circumstances only massive oral doses of aluminium are toxic and the use of aluminium in cooking utensils and cans is believed to be entirely safe.

4.2.2. Zinc

Zinc is an essential trace element, and the human body has a homeostatic (i.e. self-regulating) mechanism by which levels of zinc are regulated. Excessive intake is eliminated by enhanced excretion; consequently cases of zinc deficiency are probably more common than of zinc poisoning. Zinc intake can be important in limiting the toxic effects of cadmium.

Zinc poisoning can occur as a result of very large doses of zinc, either as inhaled fine particles (causing zinc fume fever), or by consumption of acid foods prepared in galvanized iron containers (this effect has also been ascribed to the cadmium impurity commonly present in zinc). Chronic effects from lower doses are probably of little practical revelance and copper would be expected to exert an ameliorating effect. The World Health Organisation recommended limits for zinc in drinking water relate to aesthetic and nuisance considerations, rather than toxic effects.

Overall, therefore, modest exposure to zinc is more likely to be beneficial than deleterious to health.

4.2.3 Iron and steel; stainless steel

Iron is very abundant in the natural environment and is an essential trace element for humans. As such there are well-defined problems associated with iron deficiency, and poisoning is possible but only by very large doses of iron. Accidental ingestion of ferrous sulphate tablets is a well-recognized cause of iron poisoning, especially in children. Occupational exposure to high concentrations of iron oxides in air is associated with a benign (harmless) pneumoconiosis known as siderosis.

The average adult daily intake of iron is about 500 milligrams, and exposure through use of iron in building materials is likely to provide only a very minor increment upon this intake. The World Health Organisation recommends upper limits for iron in drinking water, but as a result of taste and discoloration effects, rather than toxicity.

Steel is made by alloying iron with carbon. Other elements (e.g. manganese, silicon, chromium, vanadium, tungsten, molybdenum, titanium, niobium, phosphorus, zirconium, aluminium, copper, cobalt and nickel) may also be added to impart special properties to the steel. These are normally present at a few per cent abundance at most. Stainless steels are so called due to their corrosion-resistance. They are subject to only very slow rates of degradation due to weathering and hence release their chemical constituents at an insignificant rate. Adverse health effects due to release of minor components of steels are therefore most unlikely.

4.2.4 Copper

Copper is an essential trace element and the human body regulates its level of copper by means of a homeostatic (i.e. self-regulating) mechanism. Acute exposure to large doses of copper has known adverse health effects, but chronic (long-term) low level exposure to the metal is not believed to be associated with any ill effect.

The World Health Organisation recommends a maximum permissible level of copper in drinking water of 1.5 parts per million due to taste and discoloration effects above this level.

4.2.5 Lead

This is given detailed consideration in Chapter 5.

4.2.6 Chromium

Chromium can exist in several chemical oxidation states known as valence states. Biologically, chromium (III) and chromium (VI) are the most important and these are chemically and toxicologically distinct.

Chromium (III) is essential in animals and is absorbed only inefficiently from the diet. It is believed to be of low toxicity when consumed in modest doses.

Chromium (VI), also known as chromate, is considerably more toxic. Most of the evidence of chromium (VI) toxicity is from industries where the metal is used. The effects include:

1. Dermatitis — chromium (VI) can act as an allergen causing contact dermatitis on exposed skin. When inhaled, chromium (VI) can cause perforation of the nasal septum and inflammation of the larynx and liver.
2. Ulceration — penetration of the skin through cuts and abrasions can lead to serious ulceration.
3. Carcinogenesis — epidemiological (statistical) studies suggest that inhalation of chromium (VI) can be a cause of lung cancer (bronchogenic carcinoma). There is also slight evidence from animal studies that ingested chromium (VI) may be associated with a higher incidence of malignant tumours. There are clear indications that some chromium (VI) compounds are more potent carcinogens than others. 'Evident carcinogens' include calcium chromate, zinc potassium chromate and lead chromate.

The greatest potential exposure to chromium (VI) in the home is through old chromium based paints. The organic matrix of the paint may to some extent limit the availability of the chromium for absorption if ingested, but will not limit it entirely. It is reported (Browning, 1969) that an infant who had eaten paint containing a relatively insoluble chromium compound showed symptoms suggestive of encephalitis (a serious condition involving inflammation of the brain). Unfortunately, however, this aspect of chromium (VI) toxicity has been little investigated and it is difficult to draw firm conclusions as to the degree of risk. Chromium is not now used in domestic paints, so this problem does not exist with new paintwork.

The recommendation by the World Health Organisation of an upper limit of 0.05 parts per million on levels of chromium (VI) in drinking water is a recognition of the considerable toxicity of this chemical substance.

4.3 Uses of metals in domestic buildings

Metals are used in a wide variety of ways, some of which may lead potentially to dispersal of metallic particles within the building, others of which do not. Specific uses include the following.

4.3.1 Pipework, boilers and tanks

Pipes used for hot and cold water supply present a possible hazard due to leaching or abrasion of both external and internal surfaces. In particular, cold water pipes and storage tanks are a known source of metals in drinking water, which arise from simple dissolution of the material of the pipe into the water. Of special note in this regard are lead and copper pipes, but the materials of solders and joints must also be considered. Occasionally water drawn from the hot tap is used for cooking or drinking and in this case contact with storage tanks as well as boiler surfaces or an immersion heater element is also inevitable. The higher temperature will often lead to enhanced metal concentrations relative to cold water.

Pipes used in hot water central heating systems and for transmission of gas, as well as water supply pipes, may represent a source of metals in the home due to abrasion of outer surfaces. Such abrasion processes generally proceed at only a very modest rate and appreciable metal dispersal from this source is unlikely.

4.3.2 Ducting and flues

Ducting for hot air central heating and flue pipes are frequently of metallic construction. Metal ducting is usually concealed within walls or beneath floors and is not subject to substantial abrasion. It should not, therefore, be an appreciable source of release of metals into the building. Double-walled stainless steel is used in flue pipes. Provided it can meet the technical criteria of lack of corrosion and leakage, and adequate internal insulation to prevent risk of burning of skin coming into contact with it (stainless steel is a good conductor of heat), it provides a safe material for flue pipe construction.

4.3.3 Railings and ironmongery (hinges, window catches etc)

There are many items used in construction which come under this heading. In general, they are made of iron or steel and are subject only to mild abrasion. As such they are likely to be harmless. Use of other metals, or platings, might give cause for concern.

4.3.4 In windows (leaded lights etc)

The traditional leaded light offers some possibility of abrasion and consequent release of lead, and the opportunity of sucking or chewing by a child. Although the risk of release of appreciable quantities of lead is small, the recommendation must be against the use of traditional leaded lights. Copper, however, offers a far smaller toxic hazard and is to be preferred on health grounds.

The rationalized design (i.e. bonding the metal onto the glass), although restricting the lead to the outer surface of the glass, is nonetheless accessible, and might even part from the glass if the adhesive were inadequate. For this reason, it cannot be endorsed on health grounds. The final alternative, however, in which lead is sealed within a double glazing unit offers no hazard unless the window is broken, and then offers only a slight opportunity for exposure if replacement of the window is promptly carried out.

4.3.5 In some modern roofing materials

Plastic-coated galvanized steel and plastic-coated aluminium are used for roofing, and provide possible alternatives to roofing felts.

Clearly, if the plastic coating remains intact, there is no metal-associated hazard. If, however, the plastic coating is breached, some weathering of zinc (from the galvanization) and aluminium is certain. These are unlikely to become airborne to any significant degree; the only route of any likely importance is due to leaching by rainwater. Since both the zinc and aluminium form sparingly water soluble oxidized coatings, it is fairly certain that dissolved concentrations of metals would be modest and would represent no hazard to health, even if the drainage water were collected for drinking (indeed galvanized iron water pipes and aluminium cooking utensils are used with no known ill-effects), unless the rainwater was highly acidic.

4.3.6 Zinc, as a coating (galvanization) on iron to prevent corrosion

This should not present hazard as neither the zinc nor the iron are appreciably toxic unless ingested in considerable dosage.

4.3.7 As a component of paints

Considered in detail elsewhere (see Chapter 5).

4.3.8 As flashings on roofs

Lead is the traditional material and its low weathering rate is evidenced by the existence of intact lead sheeting on buildings of considerable age. The natural weathering processes of the atmosphere are very unlikely to generate aerosols of lead, and the hazards which exist are associated with rainwater leaching. If there is any possibility of roof drainage water being used for cooking or drinking, alternative materials should be used (although the author could find no literature indication of lead levels in roof drainage water due to use of lead flashings). In most instances, however, roof drainage water is discharged directly to a sewer or soak-away and no direct human exposure is likely. In circumstances where gutterings leak, or for some other reason lead-contaminated waters fall upon the ground around the house, some enrichment of lead in the soil is likely. On the assumption that lead weathering rates are low, however, such enrichments are likely to be small and no appreciable risks are anticipated.

The alternative materials for flashings are copper, zinc, aluminium and stainless steel. These again are unlikely to cause any air contamination, but may cause some pollution of drainage waters. Their generally low toxicities, however, give no cause for concern.

4.4 Bibliography

1. Browning, E. (1969) *Toxicity of Industrial Metals*, 2nd Edn, Butterworth, London.
2. Oehme, F.W. (ed.) (1979) *Toxicity of Heavy Metals in the Environment*, Marcel Dekker, New York.
3. Sittig, M. (1979) *Hazardous and Toxic Effects of Industrial Chemicals*, Noyes Data Corp, New Jersey.
4. Waldron, H.A. (ed.) (1980) *Metals in the Environment*, Academic Press, London.
5. World Health Organisation (1971) *International Standards for Drinking Water*, Geneva.
6. World Health Organisation (1970) *European Standards for Drinking Water*, Geneva.
7. Sax, N.I. (1979) *Dangerous Properties of Industrial Materials*, 5th Edn. Van Nostrand, New York.

5 Lead in building materials

M.F. CUTHBERT, MB BS PhD
A.N. WORDEN, MA MB BChir DVetMed PhD FRCPath FRCVS CChem FRSC FI Biol

5.1 Introduction

Lead is ubiquitous in the environment and some exposure is unavoidable. However, its importance has increased because, although the contribution from natural sources is small, industrial activity and the use of leaded petrol have increased environmental exposure. Because lead is plentiful, pliable and very resistant to corrosion and weathering it has traditional uses in building and plumbing.

Lead is present in the soil, where it has a long persistence time, and is translocated into some plants and vegetables which are eaten by animals, although surface contamination is a greater hazard. Food thus remains a major source of lead. It is not possible to remove lead completely from food but steps can be taken to reduce the lead content, for example, by avoiding the use of lead solder in tin cans and by preventing the aerial contamination of crops.

There has been much concern recently about pollution of the air by the combustion of petrol to which alkyl lead has been added to improve its octane rating since leaded petrol is the major factor contributing lead to air. In this respect the UK Government has taken the important decision to embark on a programme to remove lead completely from petrol[1], though there is an unfortunate delay in its implementation.

Another important source of lead is from its use in water systems in the form of lead pipes, connections or as linings for water tanks. In addition, lead-containing paints and primers may present a toxic hazard, particularly to young children and animals: flaking paint is a particular hazard and has been associated with many deaths in calves.

Lead occupies a unique position as an environmental pollutant because it is used and dispersed to a far greater extent than other heavy metals such as cadmium and mercury and probably has effects on health in amounts which may be encountered in the environment. Particular attention has been given to the possibility that exposure to low levels of lead may have effects on the development of children. Hence, concern about exposure to lead in the working environment has now developed into concern over low-level exposure to lead in the general environment. This is reflected in the publications in recent years, for example, reports of the Royal Commission on Environmental Pollution (Fourth Report 1974)[2], the Working Party on Lead and Health (1980)[3], the Conservation Society (1980)[4] and the Royal Commission on Environmental Pollution (Ninth Report 1983)[5].

5.2 Health effects

While the clinical manifestations of acute lead poisoning are well known, there is relatively little agreement on the effects of exposure to quantities which are usually found in the environment.

The Department of Health and Social Security set up a Working Party on Lead and Health in 1978 which reported in 1980[3]. Evidence from patients with symptoms of lead poisoning, studies on mentally retarded children, studies on patients living near smelters and general population studies in which exposure to lead as measured in the dentine of shed teeth were reviewed. In the latter respect, the study by Needleman and his co-workers[6], which was published in 1979, was particularly relevant.

The results of several new studies have subsequently been published and these have been reviewed by Rutter (1983)[7]. Although many of the reported studies measured blood lead concentrations and do not present a clear relationship between exposure to lead and effects on health, two of the reported studies[8,9] measured lead in tooth dentine and both showed a link between lead exposure and deficits in intelligence although the effects did not reach statistical significance.

The accumulated evidence, coupled with the difficulty in defining a lower limit at which exposure to lead has no deleterious effect, has served to increase concern over low-level exposure and to increase efforts to reduce lead in the general environment although none of the above studies show conclusively that exposure to lead is directly associated with defects in mental development. This is reflected in the fact that although the EEC Community Directive 77/313/EEC[10] defines a blood concentration of lead of 35 μg/dl (microgrammes per 100 ml) as an upper limit, many would assert that lower levels should be a cause for concern and recent advice from the Government[11] recommends that action should be taken to reduce environmental exposure when an individual, particularly a child, has a blood concentration in excess of 25 μg/dl. In farm animals, e.g. cattle, blood lead levels do not appear to correlate closely with lead toxicity (Dr D.L. Frape, unpublished data).

5.3 Sources of lead

5.3.1 Water supply

With specific reference to the use of lead in domestic water systems, lead is rarely present in mains water in concentrations above 10 μg/l (microgrammes per litre); well inside the level of 50 μg/l set by the EEC Directives 75/440/EEC[12] and 80/778/EEC[13]. Lead may, however, be present in water at the tap which is derived from lead in the distribution system, either from the pipes or lead-lined tanks themselves, from scale deposits which have built up in the pipes or from solder used in joints in copper pipes by hydrolytic action. It has been estimated that drinking water contributes about 10% of the total intake of lead when the water concentration is 10 μg/dl but obviously may form a much larger contribution when the water concentration of lead is elevated[5].

In 1977 the Department of the Environment (DOE) published a survey[14] on the concentration of lead in drinking water in Great Britain, conducted between 1975 and 1976, which was based on more than 3000 households. This survey showed that the majority of households had only small quantities of lead in drinking water but 7.8% of random daytime samples in England and Wales had more than 50 μg/l and 2.6% had more than 100 μg/l; levels which are unacceptable according to the EEC Directive. In Scotland the figures were higher, 34.4% exceeding 50 μg/l and 21% exceeding 100 μg/l.

Factors which may determine the amount of lead in tap water include the acidity, hardness and temperature of the water and the length of the lead piping or presence of a lead-lined tank. Soft, acidic waters, such as are found in Scotland, show the greatest tendency to leach lead from domestic plumbing, but the DOE survey showed that some hard waters also dissolve lead but to a lesser extent. The factors which influence the plumbosolvency of hard water are not well defined. Another important factor is the amount of time the water has been stationary in the water system and the temperature; in the latter respect an increase in water temperature accelerates the rate of dissolution of lead and for this reason water drawn from the hot tap is not suitable for the preparation of drinks or for cooking.

In summary, the evidence that the use of lead pipes, tanks and connections can contribute lead to drinking water in areas where the water is soft and acidic is well established. Some dissolution occurs even in hard water areas. There has been considerable effort to reduce lead contamination of drinking water in the UK by replacement of lead in water systems and by chemical treatment. In order to reduce the overall intake of lead, it is recommended that all lead-containing tanks, pipes and connections be excluded from domestic water systems in new houses; in the latter respect, the Department of the Environment have recommended that manufacturers consider the phasing out of the use of lead-based solder for connections in copper pipes[1].

5.3.2 Paint

The major use of lead in building materials, apart from those used in roofing and domestic plumbing, has been in paints, pigments, primers and driers. Leaded paint is still employed for external surfaces since it is believed to confer better weather protection and although its use in paint specifically supplied for interior decorative work has lessened, higher leaded paint is available which could be used for this latter purpose. Problems may arise from the sanding or stripping of old lead-painted surfaces, but the main significance of the continued use of leaded paint lies in its relationship to lead poisoning, principally in children. Small children may develop the habit known as pica, in which they may ingest materials not normally regarded as food-stuffs and so may chew or pick and ingest flakes of paint. Even in modern times, pica involving lead-based paint is still regarded as the most important factor in severe lead poisoning in children[15, 16]. On external surfaces in agricultural surroundings, flaking lead paint is also a hazard to livestock. Ideally, paint applied to surfaces inside or externally to which children or domestic animals may have access should be effectively lead-free and it is understood that industry is largely moving towards this goal. The lead drier levels in retail paint have in most instances declined to the order of 0.3%. This trend should be encouraged and ideally should move as soon as possible to the 0.06% as recommended in the 9th report of the Royal Commission on environmental pollution. In the meantime it is recommended that the lowest level paints available should be used. The formulation of retail gloss and varnish paints without added lead is technically feasible and it might be desirable to provide for a labelling requirement that would indicate whether any such addition had been made.

5.3.3 Other uses

There are other applications of lead for internal and external use as building materials such as in leaded lights and as flashings on roofs which could pose a theoretical risk from degradation and contamination. Leaded lights should be sealed or alternatives used. With respect to the use of lead for roof flashings, steps should be taken to ensure that the downfall does not reach water supplies or contaminate the soil and hence growing crops — although absorption from the soil by vegetables is considered to be minimal compared with cadmium.

5.4 References

1.   Department of the Environment (1983) Lead in the Environment, *Pollution Paper No 19*, HMSO, London.
2.   Royal Commission of Environmental Pollution (1974) Pollution control: progress and problems, *Fourth Report, Cmnd 5780*, HMSO, London.
3.   Department of Health and Social Security (1980) Lead and Health, *The Report of a DHSS Working Party on Lead in the Environment*, HMSO, London.
4.   Bryce-Smith, D., Stephens, R. (1980) Lead or Health (2nd Edition) *Conservation Society Working Party*, London.
5.   Royal Commission of Environmental Pollution (1983) Lead in the Environment, *Ninth Report, Cmnd 8852*, HMSO, London.

6.   Needleman, H.L., Gunoe, C.E., Leviton, A., Reed, R., Peresie, H., Maher, C., Barrett, P. (1979) Deficits in psychologic and classroom performance of children with elevated lead levels, *New England Journal of Medicine*, **300**, 689–695.

7.   Rutter, M. (1983) Low level lead exposure: source effects and implications, in *'Lead versus Health: sources and effects of low level lead exposure,'* (eds. M. Rutter and R. Russell Jones) Wiley, Chichester.

8.   Winneke, G. (1983) Neurobehavioural and neurophysiological effects of lead, in *'Lead versus Health: sources and effects of low level lead exposure,'* (eds. M. Rutter and R. Russell Jones), Wiley, Chichester.

9.   Smith, M., Delves, T., Lansdown, R., Clayton, B.E., Graham, P. (1983) The effects of lead exposure on urban children. Institute of Child Health/University of Southampton study, *Developmental Medicine and Child Neurology*, Suppl 47.

10.   Official Journal of the European Communities, **L105**, 10–12, 28th April, 1977.

11.   Department of the Environment and Welsh Office (1982), Lead in the Environment, *DOE Circular No 22/82 and WO Circular No 31/82*, HMSO, London.

12.   Official Journal of the European Communities, **L194**, 26–31, 25th July 1975.

13.   Official Journal of the European Communities, **L229**, 11–29, 30th August 1980.

14.   Department of the Environment (1977) Lead in Drinking Water, A survey in Great Britain 1975–76, *Pollution Paper No 12*, HMSO, London.

15.   Bicknell, A.O.J. (1975) *Pica. A Childhood symptom.* Butterworths, London.

16.   Billick, I.H. and Gray, V.E. (1978) *Lead based paint poisoning. Review and evaluation 1971–1977.* United States Department of Housing and Urban Development, Washington.

5.5 Bibliography

Kreuzer, W., Kracke, W., Sansoni, B. Schlachten Vermarkten. pp.393–428.

Boswell, F.C., (1975) 'Municipal Sewage Sludge selected element application to soil; effect on soil and fescue. *Journal of Environmental Quality*, **4**, 267–73.

Cannon, H.L., Bowles, J.M. (1962) Contamination of vegetables by tetraethyl lead. *Science*, **137**, p.765.

Lagerwerff, J.V., Specht, A.W. (1970) Contamination of road side soil & vegetation by cadmium, nickel, lead and zinc. *Envir. Sci. Technol.*, **4**, p.583.

Matt, K.J. (1971) Lead contamination of some agricultural soils in Western Canada. *Envir. Sci. Technol.*, **5**, p.1199.

Page, A.L., Ganje, T.L., Joshi, M.S. (1971) Lead quantities in plants, soil and air near some major highways in Southern California. *Hilgardia*, **41**, p.1.

6 Plastics and toxic chemicals

K. FLETCHER, BA PhD DipRCPath

6.1 Plastics

6.1.1 Introduction

'Plastics' is a generic term used to cover many different types of materials used in building construction. In this category may be considered such diverse products as polyvinyl chloride (PVC) used for pipework, guttering or tiling, polystyrenes for electrical fittings, foamed insulation materials such as polyurethanes or urea formaldehyde, laminates for working surfaces and many more. These materials have come into general use over the last thirty or forty years, replacing the more traditional metal and wood.

All plastics have as a basis a high molelcular weight organic polymer. These materials are themselves biologically inert and offer no hazard to health. However, on their own they are unsuitable for structural purposes and they are therefore combined with a variety of compounds to improve their performance. These include anti-oxidants and ultraviolet light stabilizers (to prevent degradation), moulding and plasticizer compounds to enable them to be formed into appropriate shapes and fillers to give mechanical strength. These additives vary widely depending on the particular plastic and its use but apart from fillers are usually present only to the extent of a few per cent of the final material.

With such a wide range of products a detailed consideration of each individual one is not feasible. It is however possible to make general estimates of possible hazards to cover most types of plastic; where specific problems have been identified these will be considered under the appropriate type.

6.1.2 Toxicity

Toxicity may arise from three different routes of exposure; ingestion of solid material, inhalation of a gas or vapour released from the plastic and contact with the skin.

The last of these is considered negligible for plastics. Except possibly in the case of floor tiling say in a bathroom, direct contact with the skin is infrequent and small; where contact is possible the nature of the material and the presence of a sealing layer precludes significant transfer of material.

(a) *Ingestion hazard*
For ingestion two types of risk may be considered, direct eating of plastic (conceivable only in the case of small children) and the drinking of water possibly contaminated with compounds eluted from plastic pipes or water tanks.

Base polymers are insoluble in water, are not absorbed and are biologically inert. For the additives an amount causing serious toxicity may be assumed in the general case to be in excess of 50 mg/kg of body weight. A 20 kg child would need to eat some 50 g of formulated plastic to obtain a toxic dose of a component present at two per cent. It is moreover likely that little of the toxic material would be absorbed from the insoluble matrix of the plastic. Given the nature of plastics used in building it is considered that poisoning by a single act of ingestion is remote and presents no significant health hazard.

It is also considered that the risk of harm by repeated acts of eating smaller quantities is equally unlikely.

Plastic tanks and pipes may be used to contain and deliver drinking water. There can therefore be a risk of toxic constituents leaching from the plastic into the water, particularly if contact is prolonged say overnight. A range of plastics for use in water storage and delivery has been tested by the Water Research Council and the British Standards Institution for the release of toxic materials. Only those approved by these bodies are considered suitable for these applications.

(b) *Inhalation hazard*

The majority of the constituents of plastics are not volatile and therefore present no risk in this context. However, there are some (e.g. phthalate esters) of low volatility which could slowly release vapour into the atmosphere. There is little or no information on the rate of release from a plastic matrix but since plastics retain their mechanical properties over many years this rate must be low. Sealing or covering the plastic will reduce this rate further. Phthalate plasticizers can occur in concentrations up to ten per cent or more in some plastics. If the floor of a room were covered in such a plastic and the plasticizer were all to be released over a ten year period, then the amount released per day could be sufficient to produce a concentration comparable to or exceeding the allowable industrial working concentration (5 mg/m^3 for di-octyl phthalate), assuming no ventilation. A lower release rate and moderate ventilation should reduce this to the acceptable level of one-tenth the above value.

Somewhat different considerations apply to other plastics. The monomer used in the production of PVC is vinyl chloride, a known human carcinogen. All PVC articles will probably contain traces of free vinyl chloride although during manufacture and storage these will be reduced to very low values especially for thin sheet or pipe. For a room floored with PVC tiles, if the tiles contained 5 ppm of vinyl chloride monomer there would be 1 ppm concentration in the room assuming complete release and no ventilation. The maximum allowable working concentration is 3 ppm. In fact release is slow, there is ventilation and the concentration of free monomer in the plastic is likely to be lower than 5 ppm. The risk of vinyl chloride is therefore very low and probably no greater than that from other carcinogens normally encountered in daily life. Since however, the risk from a carcinogen cannot be assumed to be zero at any concentration this material must be given a small risk factor.

Formaldehyde is another chemical which may cause toxicity by inhalation. Urea formaldehyde foam contains unreacted formaldehyde which is slowly released. The compound is highly irritating at concentrations above about 0.5 ppm (although susceptibility varies) and its odour is detectable below this level. Formaldehyde has been alleged as the cause of sensitization reactions and other ailments and also has been shown to be carcinogenic to animals at 6 ppm. There is no evidence that it is carcinogenic to humans. Urea formaldehyde has been the subject of much investigation and several British Standards apply. Although it is stated to be safe when properly applied, the uncertainties associated with this material neccessitate a risk rating.

For all inhalation hazards it must be emphasized that any risk is greatly reduced by adequate ventilation. Concentrations of chemicals in the atmosphere of a building will be reduced generally in proportion to the ventilation rate. Thus ten air changes a day will reduce the concentration, and risk, by a factor of ten over one change per day. For outside use where ventilation is near infinite no inhalation risk exists.

6.1.3 Composites

Plastics may be used by themselves or in combination with other materials. Thus many different types of filler can be incorporated to give desired structural properties. These are usually inorganic and may be inert or have their own intrinsic hazards such as asbestos. Plastics may also be used as laminates with other materials or with a backing. Again it should be remembered that some plastics may be painted after installation; the suitability of a particular plastic in these circumstances needs consideration. For all these types of composite the possible hazards of each component needs evaluation separately as well as in combination.

6.2 Toxic chemicals

6.2.1 Wood preservatives: insecticides and fungicides

The protection of wood against attack by insects or fungi is essential to maintain buildings in a structurally sound condition. A wide range of chemical insecticides and fungicides is used for this purpose and the two classes of agent will be considered together. For assessment of risks to health the preservatives may be thought of as falling into two categories: those that are not or negligibly volatile and those that are sufficiently volatile to have the potential for inhalational risk. In the first category are inorganic materials such as copper, tin and arsenic compounds. These penetrate the wood and in many cases combine with it chemically so that loss of chemical into the surroundings does not occur. In such circumstances absorption of the timber itself is the only means of exposure and this is extremely unlikely in significant amounts. Exposure to wood dust in repair operations normally carried out in a household is not considered to present a hazard. It should however be mentioned that the preservative solutions used can be highly toxic or irritant and should be handled carefully.

The volatile preservatives present a different problem. These include pentachlorophenol commonly used as a fungicide and the related insecticides benzene hexachloride and dieldrin. These materials, although penetrating the wood and remaining there for very many years, do nevertheless slowly volatilize continually throughout the life of the timber and are thus present in the atmosphere and are inhaled. These chemicals all possess the property of accumulating in the body over a period of exposure to levels higher than in the atmosphere. They are moreover used as biocides in materials as diverse as wallpaper paste and carpets. There is thus a possibility of some risk from a combination of all these sources.

(a) *Inhalation risk*
An idea of the risk may be gained by considering an extreme case, a room 4 m x 4 m x 2.5 m covered entirely with treated timber. The total area is 72 m^2 and the volume 40 m^3. A typical preservative formulation would contain 5% pentachlorophenol and 1% benzene hexachloride applied at the rate of 5 litres per 40 m^2. The total preservatives would be 450 g pentachlorophenol and 90 g benzene hexachloride. Assuming these volatilize completely over 30 years (the stated life for effective action) this would imply a daily release rate of 41 mg pentachlorophenol and 8 mg of benzene hexachloride. The atmospheric concentrations would therefore be roughly 1 mg/m^3 and 0.2 mg/m^3 respectively. These are to be compared with the occupational exposure limit of 0.5 mg/m^3. It is generally considered advisable that public exposure limits be at the most one-tenth of these. The extreme case levels are some 20 times those thought reasonable.

Several considerations will mitigate these values.

1. Ventilation will be far better than one air change per day.
2. A large biocide loss will occur in the first few days after treatment, before public exposure takes place.
3. Chemical will still remain in the wood even after 30 years.
4. Decorative paint films may retard loss of chemical.
5. The amount of timber considered in the extreme case is very large, although many rooms have timber floors and ceilings. As against this other sources may add to the exposure and in the case of chemicals similar in structure and effect like pentachlorophenol and benzene hexachloride it is probably prudent to take the sum of their individual concentrations into account.

Mostly in practical situations the various factors will reduce exposure to these chemicals to an acceptable level but in circumstances where large areas of timber are involved or ventilation is likely to be poor, alternatives are to be preferred. New products are continually being used and some of these such as the synthetic pyrethroids are of low toxicity and used in low concentrations. Materials like these present a lesser risk.

Where ventilation is high, as may be present in loft spaces and ground floors and certainly exteriorly the risk is negligible.

It follows from the above that extensive use of wood preservative solutions during occupancy of a building should only be done with full knowledge of the possible hazards and requisite precautions, not only for the active chemicals but also of the solvents.

6.3 Adhesives

Adhesives include a wide range of materials used in different applications; natural or synthetic rubber, polyvinyl acetate, epoxides, acrylic emulsions, phenol formaldehyde or bitumen to name only some.

By the nature of their use, adhesives are not directly accessible being concealed by the bonded material. Also the quantity of adhesive is small compared with the bonded material. Trivial exceptions occur for example in the junctions between tiles. Adhesives are in general of low toxicity and are not volatile. It is worth pointing out that while dry or cured, adhesives present no significant risk, when fresh many of them are irritant or can act as sensitizers. Bitumen is probably a low potency carcinogen so prolonged contact is better avoided. This latter property however is of little significance to the occupiers.

6.4 References

Occupational Exposure Limits. Health and Safety Guidance Note EH 40. Health and Safety Commission 1984 HMSO.

Formaldehyde and Cancer. *Lancet,* **ii,** 26 (1983).

Formaldehyde. Royal Commission on Environmental Pollution 10th Report. 124, 1984. HMSO (This report also contains a review of other aspects of indoor air quality).

Pentachlorophenol. Toxicology Review 4. Health and Safety Commission (1982) HMSO.

SECTION III

BUILDING DATA SHEETS:
Technical health and cost comparison
of materials for specific applications.

7 Use of building data sheets

7.1 Introduction

The guide is intended for use by all those involved in the design, construction, maintenance and alteration of buildings.

To derive the most benefit it is considered important readers familiarize themselves with the contents of Section II.

7.2 Layout of the sheets

Each sheet is concerned with the various materials which could be considered for use in a specific application on or within a building. The layout of the sheets is designed to permit a large quantity of information to be provided within a concise format.

7.2.1 Technical requirements

These include, where appropriate, a diagram illustrating a typical application. The technical requirements provide a brief outline of the considerations the designer may wish to bear in mind for this particular application and are based on current building industry practice. Comments are also included on the possible means of degradation of the material and potential routes of contamination to the occupants, which are provided to assist in understanding the service conditions of the material and possible means of degradation, decay and contact with the occupants. This is important as, for example, contamination of food-stuffs or water supply involves greater potential hazard to health.

The main part of the sheet comprises a column listing the material alternatives likely to be considered followed by three columns showing comments on the technical, health and cost implications respectively. This forms the basis from which the guidance notes are produced.

7.2.2 Health comment

The comments derive from the general guidance given in Section II and provide detailed consideration of the health risks, if any, of each material in each application. The risk ranking (A/B/C) is as set out below. A fuller description of this is provided in Section I.

Figure 7.1

	Potential hazard when in position	Potential hazard when chance of being disturbed	Long-term potential environmental hazard in waste disposal
	A	**B**	**C**
Non reasonably foreseeable	0	0	0
Slight/not yet qualified by research	1	1	1
Moderate	2	2	2
Unacceptable	3	3	3

Thus as an example an established safe material would rank 0 in all three categories so its A/B/C rating would be 0/0/0 whereas a very dangerous material ranking 3 in all categories would be rated 3/3/3 and so on.

7.2.3 Technical comment

Within the resources and scope of the study group detailed testing and analysis of material performance was impossible so reliance had to be put upon available technical data. The technical assessment is therefore a comparison of the materials against the 'average' conditions normally expected for each application. Thus the comments are intended to assist the designer/specifier and do not provide a definitive ranking for all circumstances. Individual designers will need to apply their own judgements in specific design situations.

A simple 1 to 10 scale is used, 1 being most satisfactory through to 10, unsatisfactory. It is assumed that all materials discussed comply with relevant British Standards and Agrément Board certificates.

7.2.4 Cost comment

As with the technical assessment this can only be used as an indicator since it is impossible to always compare like with like. For example some materials are produced in fixed modular sizes whereas others provide far greater flexibility. Cost information is important and is considered in conjunction with the health and technical comment columns in the guidance notes. Cost Data point: January 1985.

The total cost and quantity for material used in each application of a typical dwelling type are also included. The ground and first floor plans are shown in Fig. 7.2.

7.2.5 Guidance notes

These are concerned with the recommendations the authors consider to be correct based upon the information available at the time of writing.

It should should be stressed that these notes are a suggestion only. As outlined above any individual making a design judgement must consider the problem as if it occurs in that situation with his/her perception of risk in conjunction with all the other parameters affecting the decision.

The authors have however spent considerable effort in reviewing the information available and believe these guidelines to be valid. However, the authors would be grateful for any other comments and opinions.

Finally, while every attempt has been made to include all materials likely to be used in each application, absence of any other material does not mean it can be assumed to be either 'safe' or hazardous.

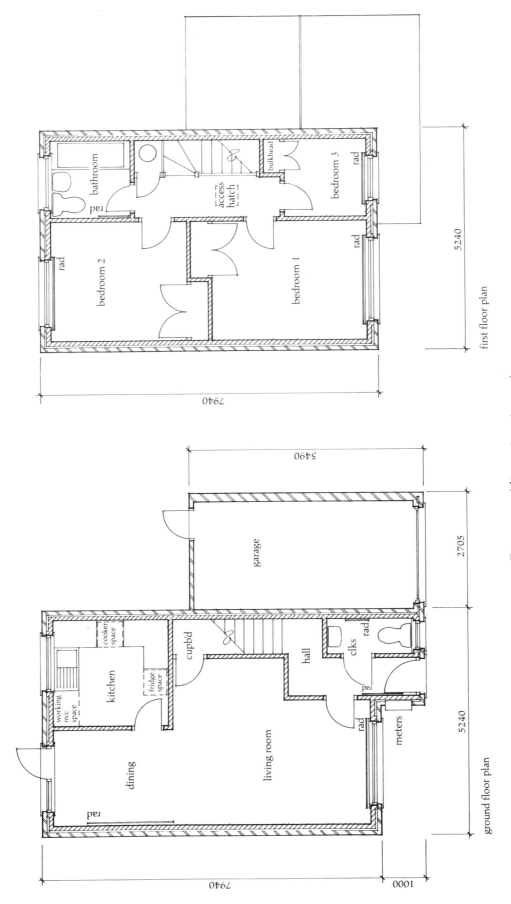

bathroom

bedroom 2

rad

rad

rad

bedroom 3

access
hatch

bulkhead

rad

bedroom 1

rad

7940

5240

first floor plan

working
m/c
space

kitchen

cooker
space

fridge
space

dining

rad

cupbd

hall

clks

rad

living room

rad

garage

meters

rad

5490

2705

5240

7940

1000

ground floor plan

Figure 7.2 (dimensions in mm)

Application 7.1
ROOFING SLATES

Typical Situation

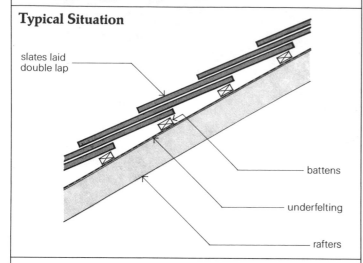

slates laid
double lap

battens

underfelting

rafters

Technical Requirements

Waterproof overlapping roof covering. Durable, impervious, rot and frost resistant. Must be resistant to ignition from fire exterior to the building. 30 year life absolute minimum, 60 plus preferred (relates to cost). Must either permit fixing holes to be made or come pre-drilled. Must not warp or bend. Must be compatible with cement mortars and metal flashings.

Decay and Degradation Factors

Normal weathering. Frost action. Fire. Abrasion from maintenance and foot traffic. Possible chemical attack by water run off from metal flashings.

Guidance Notes

From both technical and aesthetic viewpoints natural slate is to be preferred in most situations. Cost is the only negative factor.

Asbestos cement slates have been the usual 'cheap' alternative used in the past offering a good facsimile appearance to the natural material by means of colouring agents. Again there is a slight risk to the operative during cutting and fitting but discontinued use of the material for this application is strongly advised on general environmental grounds due to the potentially large area and therefore quantity of material involved and the subsequent problem of disposal in the future.

This is particularly pertinent when alternatives such as No.4 are now available with an identical appearance to asbestos cement at only modest increase in cost. The long-term durability of these new materials is expected to be closely comparable to that of asbestos cement.

With existing roofs covered with asbestos cement, abrasion and rubbing down of the surface should be avoided. The risk of exposure to fibre from the material in-situ due to weathering is not thought to be sufficiently serious to recommend immediate removal. Careful removal and disposal is necessary at replacement and demolition — see Section IV.

Alternative 6 is aimed primarily at short-life buildings where facsimile tile appearance is required at modest capital cost.

Alternatives	Technical Comment	Rank
1 Asbestos cement slate	Appearance similar to natural slate therefore has advantage as cheap replacement for this material. Acceptable life expectancy. Non-combustible.	2
2 Natural slate	Proven, very durable material. Non-combustible. Certain types, e.g. Yorkstone very heavy (*).	1 (2*)
3 Concrete slate (some referred to as interlocking tiles when laid single lap)	Interlocking concrete slates lighter than plain slates which require to be laid double lap (*). Both types give good durability and are non-combustible.	2 (3*)
4 Glass reinforced cement	Appearance similar to natural slate therefore has advantage as cheap replacement for this material. Testing indicates durability will be comparable with asbestos cement. Non-combustible.	2
5 PVA cement slates	Appearance similar to natural slate therefore has advantage as cheap replacement for this material. Testing indicates durability will be comparable with asbestos cement. Non-combustible.	2
6 Bitumen felt simulated slates	Appearance and durabililty considered to be much inferior to others. Combustible, fire properties vary. Otherwise see comments under Applications 7.9 and 7.10.	8

* Lower ranking resulting from increased weight which requires extra support.

Health Comment	Rank	Cost Comment	Unit	Rate £s	Quantity per dwelling	Total cost per dwelling £s
Asbestos release on weathering, wear, maintenance and disposal. Potential hazard from cleaning and maintenance. Problems associated with disposal.	1/3/3	610 x 305 mm slating laid on 38 x 19 mm battens using copper nails and disc rivets.	m²	15.50	80m²	1240.00
No hazard foreseen	0/0/0	610 x 305 mm blue/grey slates laid on 38 x 19 mm battens using slate nails.	m²	30.00	80m²	2400.00
No hazard foreseen	0/0/0	265 x 165 mm plain tiles laid on 50 x 19 mm battens using galvanized nails.	m²	22.50	80m²	1800.00
No hazard foreseen	0/0/0	600 x 300 mm blue/black slates laid on 38 x 19 mm battens using copper nails and disc rivets.	m²	16.00	80m²	1280.00
No hazard foreseen	0/0/0	600 x 300 mm blue/black slates laid on 38 x 19 mm battens using copper nails and disc rivets.	m²	16.50	80m²	1320.00
Refer to 7.9 Roofing felts and 7.10 Flat roof coverings asphalt and bitumen.		900 x 300 mm Glass fibre reinforced bitumen strip slates.	m²	13.50	80m²	1080.00

Application 7.2
TROUGHED SHEETING

Typical Situation

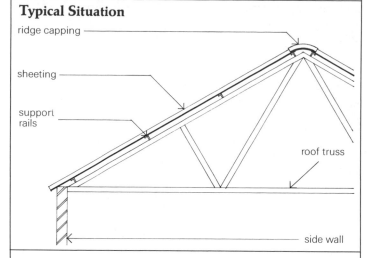

ridge capping

sheeting

support rails

roof truss

side wall

Technical Requirements

Generally applied to garage in housing (if used at all). Durable, impervious, rot, frost resistant material. Must permit site drilling for fixing and be compatible with fixing and sealants. Good fire properties, i.e. resistance to ignition, flame spread and penetration from external fire, all an advantage.

Decay and Degradation Factors

Normal weathering. Frost action. Fire. Abrasion from maintenance and foot traffic. Possible chemical attack by water run off from metal flashings.

Guidance Notes

Alternatives 2 and 3 are relatively recent developments as substitutes for asbestos cement and as such cannot be recommended unconditionally. However, durability is expected to be closely comparable to that of asbestos cement, the use of which should be discontinued on general environmental grounds.

Metal sheeting could be used successfully in this context but so far has not proved popular due to cost.

Alternatives with good fire properties to be preferred.

Guidance upon maintenance and disposal of asbestos cement shown on Application 7.1 Roofing Slates should be followed here.

Alternatives	Technical Comment	Rank
1 Asbestos cement	Good long-term durability. Limited colour range. Poor impact strength. Non-combustible.	3
2 Calcium silicate with various non-asbestos fibres	Recent development as replacement for asbestos cement. Long-term durability claimed to be comparable. Similar performance. Good fire properties. Some varieties non-combustible.	3
3 Glass reinforced cement (GRC)	Undergoing field trials at time of writing. Properties expected to be similar to asbestos cement.	3
4 Plastic coated galvanized steel	Good durability expected from currently available sheeting. Slightly easier to fix than 1, 2, 3 using self drilling, self tapping fixings. Good fire properties. Advantage of single length sheet from ridge to eaves (max 6 m).	2
5 Plastic coated aluminium	Good durability expected from currently available sheeting. Slightly easier to fix than 1, 2, 3 using self drilling, self tapping fixings. Good fire properties. Advantage of single length sheet from ridge to eaves (max 6 m).	1
6 Polyvinyl-chloride (PVC)	Suitable for glazed areas. Ranking assumes use in this context. Variable fire properties.	3
7 Glass reinforced plastic (GRP)	Usual opaque material normally only used for special features. Rarely applied to domestic buildings except for glazed areas. Variable fire properties.	3
8 PVA cement	Recent development as replacement for asbestos cement. Long-term durability claimed to be comparable. Similar performance. Good fire properties. Some varieties non-combustible.	3

Health Comment	Rank	Cost Comment	Unit	Rate £s	Quantity per dwelling	Total cost per dwelling £s
Asbestos release on weathering, wear, maintenance and disposal. Potential hazard from cleaning and maintenance. Problems with associated disposal.	2/2/3	Grey sheeting fixed with hook bolts and washers to steel purlins.	m²	10.50	20m² *	210.00
		Coloured sheeting fixed with hook bolts and washers to steel purlins.	m²	12.25	20m² *	245.00
Uncertain health status of any fibrous inclusions.	0/1/1	Standard six.	m²	12.50	20m² *	250.00
No hazard foreseen.	0/0/0	Not available until late 1985.	m²	—	—	—
No hazard foreseen in use. Slight disposal problem due to zinc content of coating.	0/0/1	0.70 mm thick sheeting secured with hook bolts and washers to steel purlins.	m²	18.00	20m² *	360.00
No hazard foreseen.	0/0/0	0.70 mm thick factory finished sheeting secured with hook bolts and washers to steel purlins.	m²	20.00	20m² *	400.00
No hazard foreseen in external application.	0/0/0	Class 3 PVC sheeting secured with hook bolts and washers to steel purlins.	m²	18.50	20m² *	370.00
No hazard foreseen due to resin base. Fibre exposure unlikely due to encasement in resin.	0/1/0	Class 3 glass fibre reinforced translucent sheeting secured with hook bolts and washers to steel purlins.	m²	18.50	20m² *	370.00
No hazard foreseen.	0/0/0	Grey sheeting fixed with hook bolts and washers to steel purlins.	m²	11.25	20m² *	225.00
		Coloured sheeting fixed with hook bolts and washers to steel purlins.	m²	13.00	20m² *	260.00

* Measured to garage only — see Figure 7.2.

Application 7.3
EAVES SOFFIT

Typical Situation

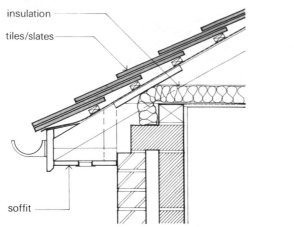

insulation

tiles/slates

soffit

Technical Requirements

Close off space at eaves between fascia and top of external wall. Span between and nail fix to rafters at normal spacing, 400 mm — 600 mm centres, without excessive shrinkage or sag. Allow provision of ventilation holes and permit decoration. Ease of cut and fit essential. Water resistance and good fire properties, i.e. not readily penetrated by or involved in fire, an advantage.

Decay and Degradation Factors

Fairly protected on underside of eaves. Abrasion from rubbing down prior to repainting. Wild life. Fire, particularly above window openings.

Guidance Notes

There is little to choose between most of the alternatives from a technical/cost standpoint. Boards which have good fire properties might be preferred technically, but due to current requirements to ventilate roofs via openings in soffits, the effectiveness of non-combustible or low flame spread materials in this location may well be negated.

As asbestos cement board is not the cheapest non-combustible alternative its use cannot be justified on general environmental grounds or on cost. It should also be noted that even though the material is not thought to pose a risk to the health of the occupier once in position it is necessary for the building operative to cut and fit the material thus putting himself at risk (unless suitable protective measures are taken). The material is also slightly more difficult to fix than the majority of the alternatives as it requires pre-drilling prior to fixing in place.

Natural finish or painted asbestos board surfaces in existing buildings should not be abraded (sanded down), drilled or cut during alterations. Careful removal and disposal is necessary on replacement and demolition — see Section IV.

Alternatives	Technical Comment	Rank
1 Asbestos cement board	Requires pre-drilling for fixing. Good fire properties, non-combustible. Precautions required for working.	3
2 Plywood	Should be exterior, WBP grade. Decoration required for protection, easy to cut and fit.	2
3 Softwood	Made up from single board or T & G boarding for wider soffit configuration. Decoration required for protection. Easy to cut and fit.	2
4 Calcium silicate board	Good workability characteristics and fire properties. Some varieties are non-combustible. Board quality determines performance so designers should select accordingly.	1
5 PVA Cement board	Good workability characteristics and fire properties. Some varieties are non-combustible. Board quality determines performance so designers should select accordingly.	1
6 Unplasticized polyvinyl-chloride (uPVC)	Some types use clip system, which requires soffit to be whole number of plank units in width as it is impracticable to cut planks along the length.	2
7 Glass reinforced cement board	Good workability characteristics and fire properties. Some varieties are non-combustible. Board quality determines performance so designers should select accordingly.	1

Health Comment	Rank	Cost Comment	Unit	Rate £s	Quantity per dwelling	Total cost per dwelling £s
Asbestos release on weathering, wear, maintenance and disposal. Maintenance potential hazard. Occupants may put themselves at risk by DIY activity. General environmental hazard.	0/3/3	12.7 mm x 225 mm board.	m	5.50	19 m	104.50
No hazard foreseen, except for very minimal risk from wood dust generated from maintenance and alteration.	0/0/0	18 mm x 225 mm BS 1455 grade 2 WBP bonded.	m	5.25	19 m	99.75
No hazard foreseen, except for very minimal risk from wood dust generated from maintenance and alteration.	0/0/0	25 mm x 225 mm boarding.	m	5.25	19 m	99.75
Uncertain health status of any fibrous inclusions.	0/1/1	12.7 mm x 225 mm board.	m	4.75	19 m	90.25
No hazard foreseen.	0/0/0	12.7 mm x 225 mm board.	m	4.75	19 m	90.25
No hazard foreseen.	0/0/0	1.6 mm x 300 mm sheet.	m	5.75	19 m	109.25
No hazard foreseen.	0/0/0	6 mm x 225 mm board.	m	4.50	19 m	85.50

Application 7.4
VERGE — PITCHED ROOF

Typical Situation

- batten
- tiles/slates
- cement mortar pointing
- rafter
- verge undercloak —bedded on mortar
- gable wall

Technical Requirements

Board material to provide neat joint at junction of roof and gable wall.
Water and rot-proof, frost resistant material required. Overhanging verge detail requires nailability for fixing. Flush verge detail shown requires key/compatibility with cement mortar.

Decay and Degradation Factors

Flush verge
Normal weathering. Frost action. Abrasion from raking out mortar.
Overhanging verge
Fairly protected on underside of verge. Abrasion from rubbing down prior to repainting. Wild life.

Guidance Notes

Here the nature of the detailing influences choice. For overhanging verge construction the detail is similar to eaves construction and therefore comments on Application 7.3 apply. With the flush eaves detail shown all alternatives other than 2 and 3 are suitable from a technical viewpoint.

The use of asbestos cement should be discontinued on general environmental grounds, although the quantity of material in this application is small, uPVC clip fit systems seem to offer many production advantages in ease of assembly and also eliminate the need for wet mortar pointing.

Designers should assure themselves regarding the frost resistance of alternatives 4 and 5 as manufacturers produce a variety of types.

Existing examples of asbestos cement in this application may have been decorated. Abrasion (rubbing down) prior to decoration should be avoided. The most practical way of removing mosses, lichens and mould growth is by chemical cleaners.

Alternatives	Technical Comment	Rank
1 Asbestos cement	Has advantage of durability in damp conditions and compatibility and ability to key with mortar. For overhanging verge would require pre-drilling for fixing.	1
2 Plywood	Only suitable for overhanging verge details where protected from weather. Must be decorated for protection. Easy to cut and fix.	2
3 Softwood	Made up from single board or T & G boarding for wider soffit configuration. Decoration required for protection. Easy to cut and fix. Only suitable for overhanging verge details where protected from weather. Must be decorated for protection.	2
4 Calcium silicate board	Manufacturers now produce purpose designed boards for external application which offer comparable durability with asbestos cement. Good workability characteristics.	1
5 PVA cement board	Manufacturers now produce purpose designed boards for external application which offer comparable durability with asbestos cement. Good workability characteristics.	1
6 Glass reinforced cement board	Good workability characteristics and fire properties. Some varieties are non-combustible. Board quality determines performance so designers should select accordingly.	1
7 Unplasticized polyvinyl-chloride (uPVC)	Made up from clip fix interlocking sections. Has advantage of eliminating need for mortar pointing. Long-term durability expected to be satisfactory. Proprietary system only suitable for use with compatible tile profiles.	1
8 Natural slate	Very durable material compatible with mortar. Disadvantage of limited length of slates requiring overlaps and careful workmanship.	1
9 Tiles (clay or concrete)	Similar durability to roof covering. Replacement awkward when damaged. Disadvantage of limited length of tiles requiring overlaps and careful workmanship.	1

Health Comment	Rank	Cost Comment	Unit	Rate £'s	Quantity per dwelling	Total cost per dwelling £s
Asbestos release on weathering, wear, maintenance and disposal. Maintenance potential hazard. Occupants may put themselves at risk by DIY activity. General environmental hazard.	0/3/3	12.7 mm x 225 mm board.	m	5.00	27m²	135.00
No hazard foreseen, except for very minimal risk from wood dust generated from maintenance and alteration.	0/0/0	18 mm x 225 mm BS1455 grade 2 WBP bonded.	m	4.75	27 m	128.25
No hazard foreseen, except for very minimal risk from wood dust generated from maintenance and alteration.	0/0/0	25 mm x 225 mm boarding.	m	4.75	27 m	128.25
Uncertain health status of any fibrous inclusions.	0/1/1	12.7 mm x 225 mm board.	m	4.25	27 m	114.75
No hazard foreseen.	0/0/0	12.7 mm x 225 mm board.	m	4.25	27 m	114.75
No hazard foreseen.	0/0/0	6 mm x 225 mm board.	m	4.00	27 m	108.00
No hazard foreseen.	0/0/0	1.6 mm x 225 mm sheet.	m	5.00	27 m	135.00
No hazard foreseen.	0/0/0	450mm x 255 mm Westmorland Green Slates.	m	9.25	27 m	249.75
		510mm x 255 mm Blue/Grey Slates.	m	6.75	27 m	182.25
No hazard foreseen.	0/0/0	265 mm x 165 mm plain tiles.	m	3.00	27 m	81.00

Application 7.5
RAINWATER PIPES & GUTTERS

Typical Situation

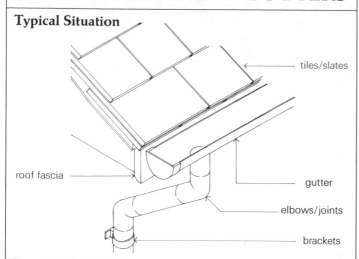

tiles/slates

roof fascia

gutter

elbows/joints

brackets

Technical Requirements

Durable and impervious gutter and downpipe. Must span recommended bracket spacing, provide easy jointing and cutting and permit decoration if required. Jointing system must cope with thermal movements. Ability to support ladder during maintenance an advantage as is resistance to impact at base of downpipe. Must be compatible with most building materials.

Decay and Degradation Factors

Normal weathering. Damage from impact near ground level. Attack by weak acid solutions in polluted environments. Mould growth, vegetation and wild life.

Guidance Notes

Selection based mainly upon appearance and cost.

uPVC now ubiquitious due to good appearance, cost factors and adequate technical performance in the vast majority of domestic applications.

Earlier uPVC systems suffered problems due to excessive thermal movement causing jonts to open but this problem has been largely overcome in currently available systems.

Asbestos cement cannot be recommended on technical, cost and health grounds.

Cast iron and timber gutters usually now only used for replacement on buildings of architectural merit where continuity of appearance is required. Use of lead for caulking spigot and socket joints in cast iron work is not recommended on health grounds.

Purpose made seamless aluminium can be produced to match cast iron gutter profiles.

Alternatives	Technical Comment	Rank
1 Asbestos cement	Needs regular painting to give good appearance. Lighter weight than cast iron. Durable except to impact resistance.	3
2 Cast iron	Durable but brittle material. Will support loads from ladder. Needs regular painting to maintain good appearance.	2
3 Unplasticized polyvinyl-chloride (uPVC)	Lightweight easily worked material. Wide range of proprietary systems now available. Improved products now appear to offer adequate durability. Painting not required.	1
4 Aluminium	Durable lightweight material. Normally available only through specialist fixers. Seamless pattern. Painting not required.	1
5 Timber (gutters only)	Regular painting required to ensure durability. Timber should be vacuum impregnated with preservative. Will support loads from ladder.	3
6 PVA cement	Needs regular painting to give good appearance. Lighter weight than cast iron. Durability comparable with asbestos cement, impact resistance slightly improved.	3

Health Comment	Rank	Cost Comment	Unit	Rate £s	Quantity per dwelling	Total cost per dwelling £s
Asbestos fibre release on weathering, wear, impact damage, maintenance and disposal. Potential hazard from cleaning and maintenance. Problems associated with disposal.	1/3/3	125 mm half round gutter on brackets screwed to timber. 100 mm diameter rainwater pipe fixed with standard galvanized pipe clips.	m m	7.00 11.00	19 m 16 m	133.00 176.00
None from cast iron, minor hazard from lead paint primer normally used on this material (see Application 7.23). Health ranking assumes lead is not used for caulking joints.	0/0/0	125 mm half round gutter on brackets screwed to timber. 100 mm diameter rainwater pipe with ears fixed with nails.	m m	10.00 17.50	19 m 16 m	190.00 280.00
No hazard foreseen in external application.	0/0/0	112 mm half round gutter on brackets screwed to timber. 110 mm diameter rainwater pipe with rubber ring 'pushfit' joints fixed with plastic coated metal holderbats screwed to brickwork.	m m	4.25 8.25	19 m 16 m	80.75 132.00
No hazard foreseen.	0/0/0	125 mm half round gutter on brackets screwed to timber. 100 mm diameter rainwater pipe with ears fixed with nails.	m m	12.00 15.00	19 m 16 m	228.00 240.00
No hazard foreseen except for very minimal risk from wood dust generated from maintenance and alteration.	0/0/0	100 x 75 mm hollowed section timber on drive in brackets; painted.*	m	6.00	19 m	114.00
No hazard foreseen.	0/0/0	125 mm half round gutter on brackets screwed to timber. 100 mm diameter rainwater pipe fixed with standard galvanized pipe clips.	m m	7.50 11.75	19 m 16 m	142.50 188.00

*N. W. England prices

Application 7.6

ROOF FLASHINGS

Typical Situation

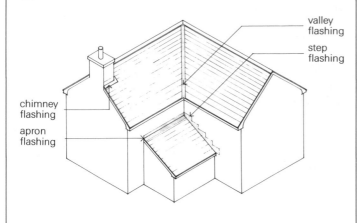

valley flashing

step flashing

chimney flashing

apron flashing

Technical Requirements

Impervious material to close off gaps at junctions of roof covering and other features. Durability must equal that of roof covering. Malleability a big advantage but non-malleability can be offset to some extent by the availability of a range of preformed sections. Must accommodate movements in the roof. Non-combustibility an advantage. Flashings should not detract from the appearance of the main roof covering or cause unsightly staining.

Decay and Degradation Factors

Normal weathering. Wild life. Frost. Bi-metallic corrosion can occur with dissimilar metals in contact but normally avoided by good building practice.

Certain grades of aluminium can be attacked by run-off from cementitious materials.

Guidance Notes

Lead finds extensive usage for roof flashings, due to its combination of excellent durability with malleability allowing it to be easily worked to form complex profiles; however, other metals are available which can be used as an alternative in most circumstances.

None of the materials in flashing applications pose a significant health hazard to the occupier. The main concern is over careless disposal of lead and asbestos fibre based materials.

However, if it is considered necessary to exclude the use of lead materials on general environmental grounds zinc is the most commonly available option, but alternatives 4 and 5 may also be satisfactory depending upon the exact detail of the flashing application. Complex pantiles profiles may still pose a problem with these materials. The main criticism of copper is the risk with certain lighter coloured open textured tiles and slates of unsightly staining due to water run-off from the flashing. This is obviously not a problem with most valley or internal gutter positions.

It is important that occupants do not collect run-off from lead-covered roofs and roofs with lead flashings for drinking purposes or for watering vegetables. Where this is expected, extra consideration should be given to the position of the flashing on the roof as there is likely to be a more concentrated flow over valleys and parapet gutters than other locations. Other alternatives might be used in this location.

Appearance may be a critical factor in selection as the majority of the options have their own distinctive character which may be used to blend or contrast with the general roof covering.

Alternatives	Technical Comment	Rank
1 Lead	In many ways the ideal material combining good malleability and workability with excellent proven durability.	1
2 Copper	Generally slightly less malleable than lead giving rise to possible problems with complex shapes. Do not mix with other metals. Detailing requires care to avoid staining caused by rainwater run-off.	2
3 Zinc	Generally slightly less malleable than lead giving rise to possible problems with complex shapes. Avoid contact with copper.	2
4 Aluminium	Malleable grades of aluminium alloy now available. Care needed in selection of quality of aluminium as it can be attacked by water run-off from cementitious material. Electrolytic action possible in polluted atmospheres, particularly when in contact with ferrous metals.	3
5 Stainless Steel	Rarely used in the past for flashings. Malleable grades now available but there may still be problems with complex shapes.	2
6 Asbestos fibre/bitumen	25 year life to be expected. Heat applied for bending but complex shapes can cause problems which can be overcome by preformed sections. Combustible.	3
7 Bitumen reinforced with aluminium foil	Available with self adhesive backing and intended as short term repair method. Useful in this context. Combustible.	8

Health Comment	Rank	Cost Comment	Unit	Rate £s	Quantity per dwelling	Total cost per dwelling £s
No hazard to occupant provided roof drainage water is efficiently and safely discharged. In this situation unlikely to pose a health hazard providing deposition on soil is avoided.	1/1/2	Code 4 step flashing with soakers. Code 4 apron flashing. Code 4 chimney flashings — apron; stepped; back and cover flashing. Code 4 valley flashing.*	m m No m	25.00 13.00 150.00 45.00	6 m 3 m 1 No 5 m	150.00 39.00 150.00 225.00
No hazard foreseen. Generally of low toxicity, unlikely to cause significant contamination of drainage water.	0/0/1	0.70 mm step flashing with soakers. 0.70 mm apron flashing. 0.70 mm chimney flashings as 1. 0.70 mm valley flashing.*	m m No m	26.50 14.00 160.00 48.00	6 m 3 m 1 No 5 m	159.00 42.00 160.00 240.00
No hazard foreseen. Generally of low toxicity, unlikely to cause significant contamination of drainage water.	0/0/1	0.80 mm step flashing with soakers. 0.80 mm apron flashing. 0.80 mm chimney flashings as 1. 0.80 mm valley flashing.*	m m No m	22.00 11.00 140.00 40.00	6 m 3 m 1 No 5 m	132.00 33.00 140.00 200.00
No hazard foreseen. Generally of low toxicity, unlikely to cause significant contamination of drainage water.	0/0/0	0.80 mm step flashing with soakers. 0.80 mm apron flashing. 0.80 mm chimney flashings as 1. 0.80 mm valley flashing.*	m m No m	21.50 11.50 150.00 39.00	6 m 3 m 1 No 5 m	129.00 34.50 150.00 195.00
No hazard foreseen. Generally of low toxicity, unlikely to cause significant contamination of drainage water.	0/0/0	0.38 mm type 304 step flashing with soakers. 0.38 mm type 304 apron flashing. 0.38 mm chimney flashings as 1. 0.38 mm valley flashing.*	m m No m	22.00 12.00 160.00 40.00	6 m 3 m 1 No 5 m	132.00 36.00 160.00 200.00
All tar products are carcinogenic but the exposure here is so low that a significant risk from bitumen is not foreseen. Presence of asbestos presents a potential hazard (see Section II .2) which depends on release with ageing, weathering and disposal.	0/2/3	4 mm step flashing with soakers. 4 mm apron flashing. 4 mm chimney flashings as 1. 4 mm valley flashing.*	m m No m	20.00 10.00 120.00 36.00	6 m 3 m 1 No 5 m	120.00 30.00 120.00 180.00
No hazard foreseen due to aluminium. All tar products are carcinogenic but exposure here is so low that a significant risk is not foreseen.	0/1/1	3 mm step flashing with soakers. 3 mm apron flashing. 3 mm chimney flashings as 1. 4 mm valley flashing.*	m m No m	15.00 8.00 90.00 27.00	6 m 3 m 1 No 5 m	90.00 24.00 90.00 135.00

* Valley flashing used as example only as not used on specimen dwelling.

Application 7.7
PIPE SLEEVE FLASHING

Typical Situation

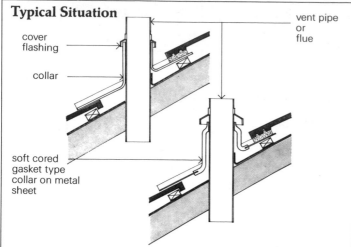

cover flashing

collar

vent pipe or flue

soft cored gasket type collar on metal sheet

Technical Requirements

At vent pipes: effective seal at the joint between pipe and roof covering. Durability same as roof covering. Accommodate movements between pipe and roof. Provide neat unobtrusive finish.

At flue pipes — as vent pipes but must be non-combustible material.

Decay and Degradation Factors

Natural weathering. Frost action. Wild life. Bi-metallic corrosion can occur with dissimilar metals.

Guidance Notes

With modern soil vent pipe (SVP) and flue pipe systems, sleeve flashings for roofs are manufactured as accessories to the system, and generally offer cost savings over the equivalent purpose-made metal (eg lead) flashings. Selection is therefore determined by/or must be related to the choice of S.V.P or flue.

However, purpose-made metal sleeve flashings still provide an effective means of sealing the joint between roof and pipe features and often offer a greater degree of flexibility where non-standard arrangements are encountered. Lead is still common probably due to availability of the material, but other metals could be utilized if required — see Application 7.6, particularly for comments regarding compatibility of metals.

Alternatives	Technical Comment	Rank
1 Lead	Traditional durable and proven material. Potential problem from electrolytic action when dissimilar metal pipes or flues are in contact with flashing.	*
2 Aluminium with flexible rubber collar	Normally used with plastics S.V.P. systems. Not suitable for flue applications. Combustible.	*
3 Glass reinforced plastic (GRP)	Material intended for use with plastic S.V.P. systems. May not be suitable for flue applications. Combustible.	*
4 Aluminium with dutrol ethylene propylene collar.	Normally used with plastics S.V.P. systems. Not suitable for flue applications. Combustible.	*
5 Synthetic rubber with flexible collar	Normally used with plastics S.V.P. systems. May not be suitable for flue applications. Combustible.	*
6 Aluminium	No problem in contact with stainless steel flue and plastic pipes. Low quality aluminium could react with asbestos cement flues.	*

* No ranking given as choice of sleeve flashing depends upon material used for flue or pipe.

Health Comment	Rank	Cost Comment	Unit	Rate £s	Quantity per dwelling	Total cost per dwelling £s
No hazard to occupant provided roof drainage water is efficiently drained away.	1/1/2	Lead slate with upstand collar.	No	22.00	1 No	22.00
No hazard foreseen.	0/0/0	450 x 450 mm aluminium slate with flexible rubber collar.	No	9.50	1 No	9.50
No hazard foreseen. Fibre exposure unlikely due to encasement in resin.	0/0/0	450 x 450 mm GRP slate with upstand collar.	No	12.00	1 No	12.00
No hazard foreseen.	0/0/0	450 x 450 mm aluminium slate with dutrol ethylene propylene collar.	No	16.00	1 No	16.00
No hazard foreseen.	0/0/0	450 x 450 mm neoprene slate with flexible collar.	No	15.50	1 No	15.50
No hazard foreseen.	0/0/0	450 x 450 mm aluminium slate with upstand collar.	No	23.00	1 No	23.00

Application 7.8

ROOF INSULATION

Typical Situation

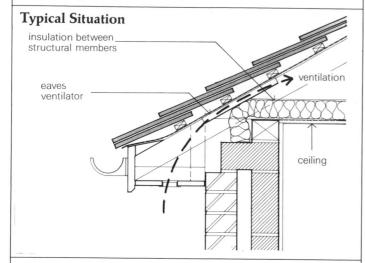

insulation between structural members

eaves ventilator

ventilation

ceiling

Technical Requirements

Rot-proof insulation for laying over ceiling between joists to provide overall minimum roof U value of 0.35 W/m²°C. Water resistance and non-combustibility an advantage. Must be dimensionally stable.

Decay and Degradation Factors

Wild life. Interstitial condensation. Fire. Contact with occupants every time access made into roof space. Dust turbulence due to effective ventilation required to prevent condensation. Contamination of water supply via uncovered water storage tank by dust particles and fibres.

Guidance Notes

The choice between the alternatives depends upon the importance ascribed to non-combustibility of the insulation, but this is not mandatory in the domestic situation.

Some samples of vermiculite have been found to contain asbestiform fibres which is a cause for concern with this material. It should only be specified when manufacturers/suppliers can show that the material does not contain respirable fibres especially the very fine fibres below 0.5 μm in diameter (specifiers should note that electron microscopy is necessary to test for this).

Loose fill granular/bead types have a small advantage due to the relative ease of installation in the confined spaces of loft areas, but this is offset by the risk of the 'sand dune' effect due to the ventilation required for condensation control.

It is essential to seal all holes/ducts entering the roof space from the interior to prevent loss of loose fill, fibres etc and also to reduce ingress to the habitable spaces. It should be noted that none of the common applications can be described as having no risk. Although the risk rating for mineral fibre represents only a suspicion, this has to be balanced against the hazard in the event of fire from the main alternatives.

Alternatives	Technical Comment	Rank
1 Mineral wool quilt	Non-combustible. Material compacts over time thereby reducing insulation value.	1
2 Loose mineral fibre		1
3 Cellulose fibre	Must have insecticidal and fungicidal protection for long-term durability. Combustible. Available with various fire properties.	2
4 Polystyrene beads	Sand dune effect from strong air movement in roof space. Slight reaction with PVC sheathed cables. Combustible. Available with various fire properties.	2
5 Polyurethane granules	Sand dune effect less of a problem due to shape of granules. Combustible. Available with various fire properties.	2
6 Vermiculite	Can absorb moisture, lowering insulation property. Poor level of insulation for similar thickness of alternative material. Sand dune effect from strong air movement in roof space. Non-combustible.	3

Health Comment	Rank	Cost Comment	Unit	Rate £s	Quantity per dwelling	Total cost per dwelling £s
Slight fibre release during access to loft maintenance, DIY and via structural gaps.	0/1/1	100 mm quilt.	m²	3.75	40m²	150.00
Roof ventilation also a factor in potential exposure. Skin, eye and throat irritation possible. Essential to avoid contamination of water systems. Long-term risks from fine fibres unlikely but not yet fully determined.	0/1/1	100 mm loose fill.	m²	1.75	40m²	70.00
Fibre toxicity not ascertained. Dust may enter living areas. Insecticides and fungicides may present hazard.	1/1/1	100 mm blown.	m²	3.75	40m²	150.00
No health hazard foreseen except in event of fire.	0/2/0	100 mm loose fill.	m²	2.75	40m²	110.00
Slight risk of sensitization. Additional health hazard if involved in fire.	1/2/0	100 mm loose fill.	m²	4.10	40m²	164.00
If asbestiform fibrous dust involved then hazardous. If it can be shown after examination using electron microscopy that there are no such fibres the rating would be 0/0/0.	3/3/3	100 mm loose fill.	m²	3.75	40m²	150.00

Application 7.9
ROOFING FELT

Typical Situation

WARM ROOF
- solar protection
- 3 layer felt
- insulation (rigid board)
- vapour barrier
- deck (concrete, steel, aluminium. woodwool)

- solar protection
- 3 layer felt
- timber deck
- insulation
- vapour check
- ceiling

COLD ROOF

Technical Requirements

Waterproof flexible materials normally in 3 layer combinations set in hot bitumen compound. Durable, impervious, rot and frost-resistant material required. Roof covering system must be resistant to ignition from fire exterior to the building. Single layer also used as underfelting on pitched roofs, normally textile fibre based. Must resist thermal movements of daily and seasonal cycles. Must be compatible with cement mortars and metal flashings.

Decay and Degradation Factors

Normal weathering — note protected from UV by solar protective layer (paint or white spar chippings). Frost action. Possible chemical attack by run off from metal flashings. Abrasion from foot traffic and maintenance. Mould growth, vegetation and wild life. Fire.

Guidance Notes

It is extremely difficult to give detailed guidance as roof covering specifications must be related to the type of decking, type of insulation and its position within the roof structure. Generally a good quality flat roofing specification should consist of 3 layers, at least one being high performance quality. In such a system the other layers would consist of glass fibre based felt as textile fibre has poor durability and asbestos fibre based ought not to be utilized on general environmental grounds.

    The main problem with existing roofs is identifying whether asbestos fibre based felt has been used. It is believed that these felts never accounted for more than 20% of the roofing felt utilized in the UK. Design drawings and specifications will be a major source of information. Avoid unnecessary abrasion upon repair, maintenance and removal. Asbestos fibre material must be disposed of carefully — see Section IV.

Alternatives	Technical Comment	Rank
1 *BS747 Bitumen felts*		
(a) Textile fibre base	Very poor durability, not used for roofs of good quality.	8
(b) Glass fibre base	Fibre base is rot proof giving improved durability. Not suitable for mechanical anchorage to deck.	3
(c) Asbestos fibre base	Fibre base is rot proof. Main advantage is improved resistance to flame penetration, but this requirement can be achieved by other types using mineral aggregate solar protection.	3
2 *High Performance*		
(a) Pitch polymer	Long-term durability still to be established but testing indicates durability will exceed that of BS747 felts.	1
(b) Polyester base		1

* See also: Application 7.10 Flat roof coverings, asphalt and bitumen.

Health Comment	Rank	Cost Comment	Unit	Rate £s	Quantity per dwelling	Total cost per dwelling £s
All tar products (e.g. bitumen) are carcinogenic but the exposure here is so low that a significant risk to the occupants is not foreseen. Material is highly inflammable.						
No extra hazard due to fibre base.	0/1/1	Three layer flat covering.	m^2	12.50	50m^2	625.00
Diameter of fibre will determine the potential or suspected hazard (see Section III 3.5). Sealed but subject to weathering. Minimal exposure to fibres.	0/1/1	Three layer flat covering.	m^2	13.50	50m^2	675.00
Age and attrition may release fibre (see Section II 2.1). Problems with disposal.	0/3/3	Three layer flat covering.	m^2	17.50	50m^2	875.00
Minimal hazard foreseen.	0/1/0	High performance pitch polymer based 3 layer built up roofing.	m^2	37.50	50m^2	1875.00
No extra hazard due to fibre base.	0/1/1	High performance polyester based 3 layer built up roofing.	m^2	20.50	50m^2	1025.00

Application 7.10

FLAT ROOF COVERINGS – ASPHALT & BITUMEN

Typical Situation

vapour barrier set in bitumen compound
rigid insulation
asphalt, 20mm in two layers
or 3 layer felt in bitumen compound
stone chippings set in bitumen compound

structural deck

WARM ROOF

Technical Requirements

Asphalt waterproof membrane of long durability (30 years expected) with good crack and puncture resistance. Must be laid on separating layer.

Bitumen As above but bitumen solutions used as adhesive for built-up felt systems — see Application 7.9.

Both materials require solar protection to reduce ultraviolet light degradation.

Decay and Degradation Factors

Natural weathering. Wild life. Maintenance foot traffic. Frost. Run-off from metal flashings. Fire.

Guidance Notes

No hazard to the occupier is foreseen with these materials in normal service conditions. However, this application should be read in conjunction with Application 7.9 dealing with roofing felts as these are used either as a separating layer with asphalt construction or as part of built-up felt systems bonded with hot bitumen. Comments on Application 7.9 therefore may apply here.

    In addition, technical experience with single layer roofing membranes is so variable that it is difficult to give an unconditional recommendation for such construction.

    Troughed steel and aluminium available for certain manufacturers can now be laid to a very low pitch approximately 4° to 6° to the horizontal and thus might be considered as an alternative to membrane construction.

Alternatives	Technical Comment	Rank
1 Asphalt	Normally used on decks of heavyweight construction such as concrete roofs. Problems can arise with roofs of lightweight construction due to excessive movement.	1
2 Bitumen (with felt in built up systems see Application 7.9)	Past experience indicates this form of construction has poor durability but all indications are that the new high performance felts have a much improved life, particularly on lightweight construction.	2
3 Single layer plastics and butyl rubber systems	Relatively little experience in the UK with these systems. Can perform well but require very careful application for success.	3
4 Troughed steel and aluminium cladding	Not a true alternative for the flat roof systems but can now be laid to a 4° pitch provided joints sealed with mastic. Durability related to effectiveness of mastic seal and life of mastic. Noise drumming may be a problem.	*

* Proved durable at steeper pitch, i.e. 10° plus, but success at low pitch still to be established.

Health Comment	Rank	Cost Comment	Unit	Rate £s	Quantity per dwelling	Total cost per dwelling £s
Hazard to occupier remote.	0/0/0	20 mm two coat mastic asphalt to BS 1162.	m²	18.25	50m²	912.50
Hazard from bitumen to occupier remote. Hazard from combination with felt. See Application 7.9.	0/0/0	Three layer built-up felt roofing: i. Textile fibre base ii. Asbestos fibre base	m² m²	12.50 17.50	50m² 50m²	625.00 875.00
No hazard foreseen.	0/0/0	Single layer roofing.	m²	24.00	50m²	1200.00
No hazard foreseen.	0/0/0	0.90 mm thick aluminium troughed sheeting and pointing with mastic.	m²	19.00	50m²	950.00

Application 7.11
FLAT ROOF PROMENADE TILES

Typical Situation

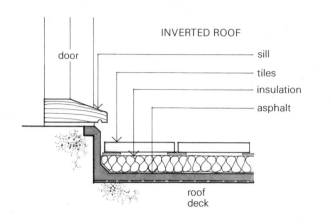

INVERTED ROOF

door — sill
— tiles
— insulation
— asphalt

roof
deck

Technical Requirements

Paving to cover walkways etc. on flat roofs. Durable, rot and frost resistant material required. Lightweight types must permit bonding and be resistant to attack by bitumen solutions. Provide protection to the roof membrane from damage and solar radiation. Slip resistance important. Good fire properties (ie resistance to ignition) may be required.

Decay and Degradation Factors

Normal weathering. Frost. Fire. Mould growth, vegetation and wild life. Abrasion from maintenance and foot traffic.

Guidance Notes

For lightweight roof construction GRC has a major advantage. With heavyweight concrete decks selection is dictated to some degree by membrane design, eg heavyweight concrete slabs are required as ballast over insulation on inverted roof construction. The risk from existing sound asbestos cement tiles is not thought to be sufficiently serious to recommend immediate removal, which would be best left until major roof overhaul. Care should be taken on removal to preserve integrity of tiles. Dispose of properly — see Section IV. Do not abrade for cleaning and maintenance.

Alternatives	Technical Comment	Rank
1 Asbestos cement	Material commonly selected in the past due to combination of good durability and lightness in weight. No longer available.	1
2 Glass reinforced cement (GRC)	Replacement material for asbestos cement. Weight similar and durability expected to be comparable.	1
3 Concrete slabs	Heavyweight compared with alternatives.	3
	Selection between types influenced by construction of flat roof deck and type of membrane utilized.	

Health Comment	Rank	Cost Comment	Unit	Rate £s	Quantity per dwelling	Total cost per dwelling £'s
Fibre release from wear, tear and maintenance. Disposal problem (see Section IV).	1/3/3	300 mm x 300 mm x 8 mm tiles bedded and jointed in hot bitumen.	m^2	24.00	50m^2	1200.00
No hazard foreseen.	0/0/0	300 mm x 300 mm x 13 mm tiles bedded and jointed in hot bitumen.	m^2	24.75	50m^2	1237.50
No hazard foreseen.	0/0/0	600 mm x 600 mm x 50 mm slabs bedded and jointed in hot bitumen.	m^2	9.00	50m^2	450.00

Application 7.12
CAVITY WALL INSULATION

Typical Situation

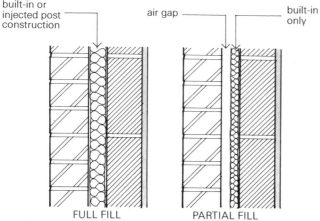

built-in or injected post construction | air gap | built-in only

FULL FILL   PARTIAL FILL

Technical Requirements

Rot resistant insulating material which combined with other wall materials must give a minimum U value of 0.6 W/m²°C. Material to be water resistant, not encourage moisture penetration. Compatibility with masonry materials and mortar essential. Must not cause premature corrosion of wall ties. Non-combustibility an advantage.

Decay and Degradation Factors

Electrical, plumbing and general building alterations can cause access to insulation. Gas or other vapours can be released into habitable rooms. Possible vapour release from insitu foam types.

Guidance Notes

In terms of weather resistance the decision on insulation is based upon the expected exposure (ie rainfall, location, local topography) together with the materials comprising each leaf of the wall. In cases of normal or sheltered exposure both partial and full fill are suitable provided workmanship is adequate. In cases of extreme exposure partial fill is to be preferred in principle as the cavity is retained.

In terms of thermal performance the choice will be influenced by the thermal resistance of the entire wall and the relationship between capital and running costs. However, for many projects limited, due to capital cost considerations, to the minimum standards of the building regulations there is little to choose between the alternatives. (The minimum standard can also be achieved using certain types of lightweight insulating blocks).

Poor workmanship can be a significant cause of damp penetration with both fill configurations (as it can be with walls without added insulation). Full and partial fill using boarded insulation and urea-formaldehyde foam require particularly good workmanship by the bricklayer and/or applicator. Poor sealing around joist ends, at eaves and around openings etc may also permit fibre and foam ingress to the interior.

In the case of urea-formaldehyde foam good workmanship is also necessary to control the possible release of excess formaldehyde gas. The combination of these factors calls into question the use of this material whose main advantage is that of low cost.

In general terms non-combustible material has an advantage. Loose mineral wool, alternative B5, appears therefore to offer the best cost/technical/health compromise. It should be noted however that non-combustibility is not mandatory and in this location the protection offered by the inner masonry leaf is considered to reduce the hazard from toxic fume to an extremely low level.

Alternatives	Technical Comment	Rank
A Built-in as Wall Proceeds		
1 Mineral wool fibre board	Non-combustible	2
2 Polystyrene bead-board	Combustible, but protected by wall. Available with various fire properties.	2
3 Extruded polystyrene board	Waterproof material. Combustible, but protected by wall. Available with various fire properties.	2
4 Polyurethane foam board	Waterproof material. Combustible, but protected by wall. Available with various fire properties.	2
5 Polyisocy-anurate board	Offers slightly higher standard of insulation for equivalent thickness to other materials. Waterproof material. Combustible, but protected by wall. Available with various fire properties.	2
B Injected after Construction		
1 Urea-formaldehyde foam	Combustible, but protected by wall. Poor application leads to cracks in foam, which in turn can cause water penetration. Site quality control vital.	3
2 Loose fill polystyrene beads	Beads can fall out when openings made for services or alterations. Combustible, but protected by wall.	2
3 Bonded polystyrene beads	Adhesive injected with beads overcomes problem of loose fill. Combustible, but protected by wall.	1
4 Polyurethane foam chips	Shape and size of chips reduces tendency to fall out when openings made for services and alterations. Combustible, but protected by wall.	2
5 Loose mineral wool	Non-combustible. Can be removed if required.	1
6 Cellulose fibre	Not commonly used for this application. Fibre could decay in damp conditions, therefore, must have insecticidal and fungicidal protection. Combustible, but protected by wall.	6

Health Comment	Rank	Cost Comment	Unit	Rate £s	Quantity per dwelling	Total cost per dwelling £s
Potential fibre release from structural gaps, maintenance and DIY work. Exposure likely to be extremely low due to location of material, but skin, eye and throat irritation possible. Long-term risks from fine fibres unlikely but not yet fully determined.	0/1/1	50 mm thick board.	m^2	2.75	$137m^2$	376.75
No health hazard foreseen except in the event of fire where risk from toxic fumes is minimal due to cavity wall construction.	0/1/0	50 mm thick board.	m^2	2.00	$137m^2$	274.00
	0/1/0	50 mm thick board.	m^2	3.25	$137m^2$	445.25
	0/1/0	50 mm thick board.	m^2	8.50	$137m^2$	1164.50
	0/1/0	50 mm thick board.	m^2	7.00	$137m^2$	959.00
Health risk not fully ascertained. In the event of fire risk from toxic fumes is minimal due to cavity wall construction. Slight risk of sensitization.	1/1/0	50 mm cavity.	m^2	2.75	$137m^2$	376.75
No health hazard foreseen except in the event of fire where risk from toxic fumes is minimal due to cavity wall construction.	0/1/0	50 mm cavity.	m^2	2.50	$137m^2$	342.50
	0/1/0	50 mm cavity.	m^2	3.00	$137m^2$	411.00
	0/1/0	50 mm cavity.	m^2	2.75	$137m^2$	376.75
Potential fibre release from structural gaps, maintenance and DIY work. Exposure likely to be extremely low due to location of material, but skin, eye and throat irritation possible. Fine fibre safety not yet determined.	0/1/1	50 mm cavity.	m^2	2.25	$137m^2$	308.25
Toxicity not yet appraised. Insecticides and fungicides may present hazard.	1/1/1	Price not available.	—	—	—	—

Application 7.13

TIMBER FRAMED WALL INSULATION

Typical Situation

- plywood sheathing
- vapour barrier (polythene)
- insulation between timber framing
- plasterboard lining
- D.P.C.
- concrete floor

Technical Requirements

Rot-resistant insulating material which combined with other materials of the wall must give a minimum U value of 0.6W/m²°C. Resistance to moisture absorption advantageous. Non-combustible material desirable and necessary in party walls. Provides essential part of sound insulation of party wall.

Decay and Degradation Factors

Electrical and plumbing alterations can cause access to insulation both by building operatives and DIYs. Interstitial condensation risk with substandard workmanship. Fire.

Guidance Notes

Although the insulation receives some protection from the plasterboard lining in the event of a fire it is still desirable to use a non-combustible insulation in this application and therefore mineral and glass wool seem most suitable.

    The health risk rating for mineral fibre results from the slight suspicion over this material pending the completion of toxicological and epidemiological studies.

    Good workmanship is essential with this type of construction to ensure effective installation of the vapour barrier and thus eliminate potential condensation problems. The vapour barrier should eliminate fibre ingress to the interior.

Alternatives	Technical Comment	Rank
1 Mineral and glass wool	Available as quilt or board. Has major advantage of non-combustibility in this application.	1
2 Expanded polystyrene	Combustible, but material is protected by plasterboard lining. Available with various fire properties.	3
3 Polyurethane foam	Combustible, but material is protected by plasterboard lining. Available with various fire properties.	3
4 Polyisocy-anurate foam	Combustible, but material is protected by plasterboard lining. Available with various fire properties.	3

Health Comment	Rank	Cost Comment	Unit	Rate £s	Quantity per dwelling	Total cost per dwelling £s
Potential fibre release from structural gaps, maintenance and DIY work. Minimal exposure likely but skin, eye and throat irritation possible during DIY. Long-term risks from fibres unlikely but not yet fully determined.	0/1/1	100 mm mineral fibre board and fix vertically between battens.	m²	4.25	133m²	565.25
		100 mm paper faced mineral fibre board and fix vertically between battens.	m²	4.75	133m²	631.75
No health hazard foreseen if material in situ. If involved in fire additional health hazard resulting from toxic fumes.	0/2/0	50 mm thick board.	m²	4.00	133m²	532.00
Slight risk of sensitization. If involved in fire additional health hazard resulting from toxic fumes.	1/2/0	50 mm thick board.	m²	7.50	133m²	997.50
Slight risk of sensitization. If involved in fire additional health hazard resulting from toxic fumes.	1/2/0	50 mm thick board.	m²	8.25	133m²	1097.25

Application 7.14

SEALANTS TO DOOR & WINDOW FRAMES

Typical Situation

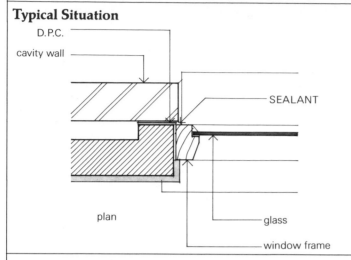

Technical Requirements

Provide impervious draught seal between frames and structure. Must be rot and frost resistant and cope with movement. Good appearance necessary or be able to take decoration. Capable of adhering to a wide range of materials, and must not slump at high temperatures.

Decay and Degradation Factors

Normal weathering. Frost. Maintenance and decoration. Mould growth, vegetation and wild life. Cleaning and cleaning solutions.

Guidance Notes

Technical performance is normally related to cost ie the lower the cost the lower the life expectancy. Formulations using asbestos as a filler or lead as a drying agent could pose a slight hazard but if one considers the small quantities used in the domestic situation the risk is virtually insignificant to the occupant, provided dry sanding is not used as a means of preparation for decoration. The best method of removal is by raking out.

　　Most types do not contain these materials but if it is necessary to avoid all possible risk manufacturers should be consulted to confirm the contents of their formulations.

Alternatives	Technical Comment	Rank
Sealants usually based on one or more of the following:	Various formulation combinations are available from manufacturers. Generally satisfactory for domestic use. Life expectancy given in BS 6213 as	
1 Acrylic	up to 15 years	2
2 Synthetic rubber	up to 10 years	3
3 Expoxy resins	none given in BS 6213 but expected to last well	2
4 Polysulphide	up to 20 years	1
5 Polyurethane	up to 20 years	1
6 Silicone	up to 20 years	1
7 Oleo-resinous (oil)	up to 10 years	3
	Grading based on life expectancy, but other factors such as ease of application may influence choice	

Health Comment	Rank	Cost Comment	Unit	Rate £s	Quantity per dwelling	Total cost per dwelling £s
		Supply only.	10 litres	58.75	2 litres	11.75
		Supply only.	10 litres	32.75	2 litres	6.55
No hazard foreseen once cured except formulations using asbestos fibre as filler or lead as the drying agent. See Application 7.15 — glazing putty.		Supply only.	10 litres	95.25	2 litres	19.05
		Supply only.	10 litres	67.50	2 litres	13.50
Due to numerous products available composition should be clarified prior to specification.		Supply only.	10 litres	41.75	2 litres	8.35
		Supply only.	10 litres	93.25	2 litres	18.65
		Supply only.	10 litres	25.75	2 litres	5.15

Application 7.15
GLAZING PUTTY

Typical Situation

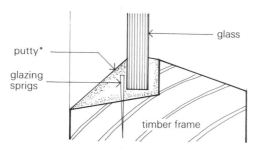

*Gloss painting required 7 days after application to avoid rapid hardening of linseed oil putty.

Technical Requirements

Soft easily worked compound to fix glazing in place. Must harden sufficiently to hold glass but still remain sufficiently soft to remain an effective air and water seal and accommodate movements between glass and timber frame. Ability to receive decoration essential.

Decay and Degradation Factors

Natural weathering. Frost action. Wild life. Abrasion (sanding) prior to repainting. Periodic replacement through damage to glass or normal ageing. Cleaning and cleaning solutions.

Guidance Notes

In most circumstances for single glazing into painted timber frames unleaded linseed oil putty will prove most appropriate and cost effective.

Specifiers should note that frames must be primed before glazing to prevent loss of oil into the timber and that the finished putty should be painted approximately 7 days after application to prevent loss by evaporation.

When using unpainted ie woodstained frames and when double glazing using glazing beads synthetic rubber based compounds are to be preferred. Some of these formulations containing asbestos may pose a slight risk during maintenance work so in circumstances where it is necessary to avoid all risk it will be necessary to check with manufacturers as there are asbestos-free alternatives available.

Although leaded linseed oil putty has not been available from reputable manufacturers for some time it seems wise when undertaking maintenance work to consider that existing putty will have a lead content and to treat the material in a similar manner to lead-based paints as described in Section IV ie avoiding dry sanding as a means of preparation or removal.

Alternatives	Technical Comment	Rank
1 Leaded linseed oil putty	Not available from reputable manufacturers.	—
2 Unleaded linseed oil putty	Satisfactory for general domestic applications to painted frames.	1
3 Synthetic rubber base glazing compound	Satisfactory for general domestic applications but can also be used for unpainted timber frames protected by decorative wood stains.	1
4 Polysulphide base glazing compound	Satisfactory for general domestic applications but can also be used for unpainted timber frames protected by decorative wood stains.	1

Health Comment	Rank	Cost Comment	Unit	Rate £'s	Quantity per dwelling	Total cost per dwelling £s
If in accessible location, significant hazard to children by ingestion. Sanding down for maintenance may release lead dust.	3/3/3	Supply only.	12.5 litres	9.00	2.25 litres	1.62
No hazard foreseen.	0/0/0	Supply only.	12.5 litres	9.00	2.25 litres	1.62
Certain formulations contain a small quantity of asbestos fibre which could be released by sanding down for maintenance. If asbestos free, no hazard foreseen.	0/3/3 0/0/0	Supply only.	12.5 litres	13.00	2.25 litres	2.34
Certain formulations use lead driers. Lead dust could be released by maintenance. If lead free, no hazard foreseen.	* 0/0/0	Supply only.	12.5 litres	86.00	2.25 litres	15.48

*Grading depends upon % content of lead. See Application 7.23.

Application 7.16

PATENT GLAZING

Typical Situation

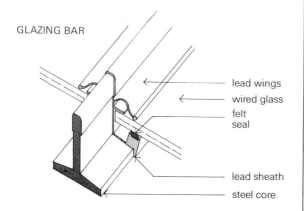

GLAZING BAR

— lead wings
— wired glass
— felt
— seal

— lead sheath
— steel core

Technical Requirements

Method of constructing glazed areas giving minimum interruption to glazing ie minimum size of glazing bar. Bars to be corrosion free, with adequate strength characteristics and ability to provide sealed cladding to resist air and rain penetration. Tidy visual appearance and convenient fixing required.

Decay and Degradation Factors

Abrasion (sanding) if decoration required. Natural weathering. Frost action. Wild life. Corrosion. Aggressive water run-off from cementitious materials and metal flashings. Cleaning and cleaning solutions.

Guidance Notes

For the majority of existing lead-covered steel patent glazing there is little hazard where the material is used for inaccessible roof glazing and remains undisturbed. However, this construction was used for a variety of glazed areas, such as conservatories, and might therefore be accessible. Rubbing down or abrasion for decoration and cleaning purposes should be avoided. Consideration could also be given to sealing the lead by means of varnish or paint. Secondary windows would prevent children coming into contact with accessible glazing bars.

Alternatives	Technical Comment	Rank
1 Steel bars with lead wings and sheathing	Traditional method, no longer available.	—
2 Steel bars with PVC wings and sheathing	Technically superior to traditional method as latest types permit use of double glazed units.	1
3 Aluminium bars and wings with neoprene seals	Technically superior to traditional method as latest types permit use of double glazed units.	1

Health Comment	Rank	Cost Comment	Unit	Rate £s	Quantity per dwelling	Total cost per dwelling £s
Hazard where lead is accessible to children. Possible contribution to dust due to abrasion resulting from cleaning and maintenance. Do not collect water run-off from areas of patent glazing for drinking purposes.	2/2/2	Glazing bars spanning 2m; glazed with georgian wired cast glass.	m²	66.00*	10m²	660.00
No hazard foreseen.	0/0/0	Glazing bars spanning 2 m; glazed with georgian wired cast glass.	m²	77.00*	10m²	770.00
No hazard foreseen.	0/0/0	Glazing bars spanning 2 m; glazed with georgian wired cast glass.	m²	57.25*	10m²	572.50

* Nominal measurement only

Application 7.17

LEADED LIGHTS

Typical Situation

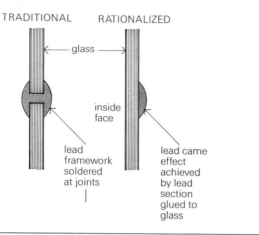

TRADITIONAL   RATIONALIZED

glass

inside face

lead framework soldered at joints

lead came effect achieved by lead section glued to glass

Technical Requirements

Traditional: Water tight malleable metal framework to connect small panes into single window opening. Ideally long term durability to be as good as glass.

Rationalized: Decorative effect to achieve similar appearance to traditional by adhesive bonding metal strip onto glass sheet. Adhesive must have good durability.

Decay and Degradation Factors

Natural weathering. Frost action. Wild life. Cleaning and cleaning solutions.

Guidance Notes

With this application a particular aesthetic effect is desired.

For historic and other buildings of character it is suggested that copper be considered in preference to lead when complete replacement of the traditional came type is necessary, although specialist companies do not offer copper as a standard alternative at present.

Rubbing down or abrasion of existing lead cames for decoration and cleaning purposes should be avoided. Consideration could also be given to sealing the lead by means of varnish or paint. Abrasion should not be used to remove existing paint on lead cames. Secondary windows would prevent children coming into contact with the cames.

With modern buildings, if the leaded light effect must be provided, reproduction or facsimile appearance can be achieved by alternative 4 in preference to 3.

Alternatives	Technical Comment	Rank
1. Traditional lead	Generally used for stained glass and for replacement work on historic and other buildings of character.	1*
2. Traditional copper	Could be used as an alternative to traditional lead, but not generally available.	1*
3. Rationalized lead (lead strips bonded to face of single glass sheet)	Appearance inferior to traditional. Life related to durability of adhesive.	1*
4. Rationalized lead (lead strips sealed in double glazing)	Appearance inferior to traditional. Adhesive protected from weathering.	1*

* Ranking a compromise between both technical and aesthetic considerations

Health Comment	Rank	Cost Comment	Unit	Rate £s	Quantity per dwelling	Total cost per dwelling £s
Hazard from accessibility of lead to children. Possible contribution to dust due to abrasion resulting from cleaning and maintenance.	2/2/2	Leaded lights in rectangular panes.	m²	65.00	9 m²	585.00
No hazard in use. Less toxic than lead.	0/0/1	Coppered lights in rectangular panes.	m²	150.00	9 m²	1350.00
Less hazard if lead is restricted to external surface. Ground floor windows accessible to children.	1/2/2	Lead strips in rectangular pattern.	m²	55.00	9 m²	495.00
No hazard unless window is broken. Acceptable in normal usage.	0/1/2	Hermetically sealed units, lead strips in rectangular pattern.	m²	90.00	9 m²	810.00

Application 7.18
CEILING AND WALL LININGS

Typical Situation

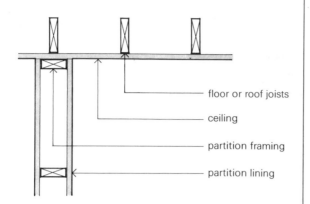

— floor or roof joists

— ceiling

— partition framing

— partition lining

Technical Requirements

Sheet material with adequate strength to span over framing members 400 – 600 mm centres. Sound insulation properties may be important. Lining may be required to contribute to the fire resistance of the floor or wall. Non-combustibility may be a requirement but good fire properties (ie resistance to ignition and flame spread) an advantage. Fire properties may be modified by decoration. Water and rot resistance an advantage.

Decay and Degradation Factors

Abrasion due to sanding, scraping to remove wallpaper and other decoration. Drilling and cutting for fixing fittings and plumbing and electrical alterations. Impact. Normal wear and tear.

Guidance Notes

Although concern has been expressed over formaldehyde gas release from the resin content of chipboard and radon emission from certain continental manufactured plasterboard the main hazard in new construction will continue to be posed by combustible materials in this application. Provided the construction conforms with building regulations only a slight risk results mainly from toxic fumes emitted by timber based materials in the event of a fire.

Plasterboard ceilings are usually utilized to provide the major element in the ½ hour fire resistance required for the timber first floor in 2 storey house construction. This material in two or more layers and/or combined with alternatives 7 and 9 can be used to provide the 1 hour(+) fire resistance for timber floors over integral garages or in flats.

Formaldehyde might become a cause for concern if two or more of the following are expected.
(a) Large areas of fairfaced chipboard (ie wall, ceiling and floor linings).
(b) Urea-formaldehyde foam insulation in cavity wall.
(c) Low ventilation rates.
A combination of these factors might cause irritation and/or reaction from sensitive individuals.

Timber boarding and timber based boards may pose a slight hazard when treated with preservatives — see Application 7.26.

Asbestos insulation board is no longer available; however, existing applications may be found in ceilings over integral garages and in ceiling and wall linings in flats built up to 1960 when asbestos-free alternatives 7 and 9 became available. In most cases the asbestos board was used to provide improved fire resistance, so if the material appears undamaged it may be sealed by means of proprietary plastic compounds. In the majority of cases removal may cause an increased hazard and the options of sealing or removal need to be considered carefully. The local environmental health officer should be contacted for advice.

Do not scrape, sand or scrub for decoration and cleaning purposes. Avoid drilling for services and fixed furniture.

If it is decided to replace asbestos insulation board in most circumstances the new lining must provide a similar fire performance. The removed material *must* be disposed of properly — see Section IV.

Alternatives	Technical Comment	Rank
1 Plasterboard	Used as dry liner decorated directly or with 3 – 5 mm skim coat of plaster applied. Good fire properties; frequently used as fire protection lining.	1
2 Timber (tongue & groove boarding)	Selected mainly for appearance.	2
3 Chipboard	Usually faced with plastic laminate, but could be used fair faced.	2
4 Blockboard	Usually faced with plastic laminate, but could be used fair faced.	2
5 Plywood	Can be used with plastic laminate facing but often used for natural appearance. V-grooved type available as cheaper substitute for T & G boarding. Thinner sheeting requires closer spaced supports.	2
6 Hardboard	Can be used with range of surface finishes. Thinner sheeting requires closer spaced supports. May need conditioning.	4
7 Calcium silicate based board	Long-term durability not determined but expected to be satisfactory in internal environment. Can be plastered if required. Good fire properties, some varieties non-combustible. Suitable for fire protection lining, especially as replacement for asbestos insulation board.	1
8 Asbestos insulation board	Non-combustible. Only used as fire protection lining, usually in flats and domestic integral garage ceilings and/or walls. Not now manufactured in UK.	2
9 Glass reinforced cement board	Non-combustible. New product, long-term durability not determined but expected to be satisfactory in internal environments. Suitable for fire protection lining as a replacement for asbestos insulation board.	—

Health Comment	Rank	Cost Comment	Unit	Rate £s	Quantity per dwelling	Total cost per dwelling £s
No hazard foreseen from UK origin plasterboard. Source of gypsum imported should be checked.	0/0/0	12.7 mm thick ready for decoration.	m^2	4.75	132m^2 *	627.00
Fine wood dust product by maintenance is a suspect carcinogen, perhaps enhanced by wood preservatives. Tropical hardwood dusts have respiratory effects.	0/2/0	19 mm tongued, grooved and V-jointed softwood boarding in 150 mm widths	m^2	10.75	132m^2 *	1419.00
		10 mm tongued, grooved and V-jointed wester red clear boarding in 150 mm widths	m^2	15.50	132m^2	2046.00
Release of volatiles on breakdown of resins, glues in man-made boards and surface treatments.	1/2/0	12.7 mm thick butt jointed plain lining.	m^2	4.25	132m^2 *	561.00
Pyrolysis produces respiratory irritants and asphyxiants.	1/2/0	12.7 mm thick butt jointed plain lining.	m^2	8.50	132m^2 *	1122.00
	1/2/0	12.7 mm thick butt jointed plain lining.	m^2	10.00	132m^2 *	1320.00
	1/2/0	12.7 mm thick butt jointed plain lining.	m^2	8.50	132m^2 *	1122.00
Uncertain health status of any fibrous inclusions. Fibre only likely to be released by machining and abrasion.	0/1/1	12.7 mm thick butt jointed plain lining.	m^2	14.25	132m^2 *	1881.00
Significant hazard. See comments under Guidance Notes.	3/3/3	12.7 mm thick butt jointed plain lining.	m^2	10.00	132m^2 *	1320.00
No hazard foreseen. Fibre only likely to be released by machining and abrasion.	0/0/0	6 mm thick butt jointed plain lining.	m^2	6.25	132m^2 *	825.00

* Measured to ceilings and first floor partitions only

Application 7.19
FLOORBOARDING

Typical Situation

- floorboarding
- floorcovering *or* direct varnish finish
- floor joists
- ceiling

Technical Requirements

Smooth floor surface. Nailable material to span normal joist spacing of 400–600 mm centres. Ease of cutting essential. Boarding contributes to fire and sound performance and total floor construction. Good fire properties (ie resistant to ignition from small fire sources and resistance to flame spread) an advantage.

Decay and Degradation Factors

Abrasion due to foot traffic will take place unless protected by floor coverings. Fire. Sanding down for re-varnishing where applicable.

Guidance Notes

This application is included due to the recent concern over formaldehyde gas release from chipboard. This would only be a problem if the use of large areas of material was comtemplated, together with low rates of ventilation — see Application 7.18.

The health risk ratings shown refer to the fire/toxic fume hazard which continues to be the main risk with this application. To avoid this the only alternative would be the use of concrete floor construction. Where the floor is finished direct, ie varnished or waxed, maintenance work requiring sanding down may cause a slight hazard from wood dust.

From a technical viewpoint selection is based mainly upon cost/convenience factors particularly in relation to access to the plumbing and wiring systems located in the floor void.

Alternatives	Technical Comment	Rank
1 Timber tongue and groove boarding (T & G)	Traditional flooring. Permits relatively easy access to floor voids for alteration and maintenance. Sound and fire performance of floor construction using T & G superior to plane edge boarding.	1
2 Chipboard (T & G edged)	Purpose made flooring sheets available. Severe dampness causes loss of strength. Sound and fire performance of floor construction using T & G superior to plane edge board, but access to floor void more difficult.	2
3 Blockboard	Rarely used for this application but could prove satisfactory. Not available as proprietary product with T & G edge.	2
4 Plywood	Greater bending strength allows greater span between joist centres.	1

Health Comment	Rank	Cost Comment	Unit	Rate £s	Quantity per dwelling	Total cost per dwelling £s
Fine wood dust produced by maintenance is a suspect carcinogen, perhaps enhanced by wood preservatives. Tropical hardwood dusts have respiratory effects. Glues, in man-made boards, resins and surface treatments may break down to produce irritant volatiles. Pyrolysis products irritant and asphyxiant.	0/2/0	25 mm wrought softwood T & G boarding in 125 mm widths.	m²	12.00	31m² *	372.00
	1/2/0	22 mm butt jointed chipboard to BS 5669.	m²	6.25	31m² *	193.75
		22 mm T & G chipboard to BS 5669.	m²	6.75	31m² *	209.25
	1/2/0	25 mm butt jointed birch faced blockboard.	m²	13.25	31m² *	410.75
	1/2/0	25 mm butt jointed plywood to BS 1088 marine grade.	m²	26.50	31m² *	821.50

Application 7.20

FIRE DOORS

Typical Situation

optional architrave

frame with screwed planted stop or machined from solid

intumescent strip*

solid core door

facing (usually plywood)

lipping

'HALF HOUR' DOOR

*Intumescent strip − needed some types of ½ hour door essential for longer periods of fire resistance.

Technical Requirements

Door and frame combination to provide ½ to 2 hour fire resistance (½ hour most common requirement with domestic applications). Construction of door together with appropriate ironmongery must provide adequate strength, racking and warp resistance for both normal usage and in the event of a fire. Combustible material permissible provided door satisfies fire test requirements. (BS 476 Part 8)

Quality of factory applied finish important or must accept decoration, using paints and/or varnishes.

Decay and Degradation Factors

Fire. Normal wear and tear, particularly impact damage. Cleaning and cleaning solutions. Abrasion (sanding down) prior to repainting.

Guidance Notes

Fire doors including asbestos insulating board are not now available. It is often difficult to identify doors with asbestos cores but provided the material is contained by facings (usually plywood) and timber lippings there should be little hazard. Although it was unusual to use asbestos board as the finished surface on the majority of doors fixed in new construction, it was fairly common to upgrade existing panel doors in refurbishment schemes by adding asbestos board to one face. This should be replaced by alternative 4. The existing asbestos material should be disposed of properly − see Section IV.

It is important that replacement doors have the same fire rating as the existing.

For the currently available alternatives technical selection depends upon apearance provided doors satisfy fire rating standards mentioned under technical comments.

Alternatives	Technical Comment	Rank
1 Asbestos insulation board	Not available.	—
2 Flaxboard core	Choice really depends upon finish and appearance required provided doors comply with BS 476 Part 8 for required period of fire resistance.	—
3 Mineral wool fibre board core		—
4 Calcium silicate board core		—
5 Blockboard core		—

Health Comment	Rank	Cost Comment	Unit	Rate £s	Quantity per dwelling	Total cost per dwelling £s
Significant hazard where insulation board forms facing of door. Where used on a core enclosed within facings and lippings, fibre release restricted.	3/3/3 0/3/3	No longer available.	—	—	—	—
No hazard foreseen except in event of fire	0/2/0	762 x 1981 mm; half hour fire resistance; plywood facing both sides.	No	77.50	*	—
Fibre contained within facings and lippings. No hazard foreseen except in event of fire but core would not contribute to toxic fumes.	0/1/1	Not yet available, but likely to be used in the future.	—	—	—	—
Uncertain health status of any fibrous inclusions, but contained within facings and lippings.	0/1/1	Not available.	—	—	—	—
No hazard foreseen except in event of fire.	0/2/0	762 x 1981 mm; half hour fire resistance plywood facing both sides.	No	73.50	*	—

* Not required in example house type Figure 7.1.

Application 7.21

FLOOR TILE AND SHEET

Typical Situation

CONCRETE FLOOR

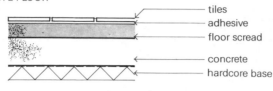

- tiles
- adhesive
- floor scread
- concrete
- hardcore base

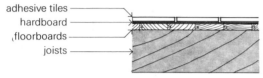

adhesive tiles
hardboard
floorboards
joists

TIMBER SUSPENDED FLOOR

Technical Requirements

Smooth but slip resistant easily cleaned surface of acceptable appearance. Hardwearing surface resistant to damage from heel load/castor etc. Resistant to water and attack by cleaning solutions, fats, cooking oils etc. Dimensional stability vital. Good fire properties (ie resistant to ignition from small fire sources and resistant to flame spread) an advantage.

Decay and Degradation Factors

Ordinary wear and tear, foot traffic and spillage. Potential attack from cleaning powders/solutions. Possible removal by DIY owner. Abrasion from furniture movement. Fire.

Guidance Notes

Technical selection depends upon required wear resistance which in turn is related to location in the dwelling (eg hall, lounge, bathroom etc) and also upon particular manufacturer's formulations. For best results refer to British Board of Agrément 'UPEC' classification.

Aesthetically vinyl and PVC types may be preferred due to wider colour ranges.

Manufacturer's formulations vary but generally PVC floorings are more flexible than the alternatives which may have implications on the standard of workmanship needed in the sub-base. PVC types can also be site welded to produce large areas of continuous flooring.

As there is a slight risk of fibre release with normal wear and tear and a significant risk of release at replacement which is likely to occur at least once during the life of the building the use of vinyl asbestos is strongly discouraged. Special precautions should be taken when removing this material which should be disposed of carefully — see Section IV.

It is difficult to counsel removal of existing vinyl asbestos material purely upon health grounds as the removal process will probably generate greater hazard than covering and sealing with an alternative floor finish.

Alternatives	Technical Comment	Rank
1 Vinyl, asbestos fibre	Suitable for all domestic applications. Better abrasion characteristics than thermoplastic. Good fire properties.	1
2 Vinyl, mineral fibre (asbestos free)	Recent introduction as substitute for vinyl asbestos. Long-term durability expected to be similar. Suitable for all domestic applications. Good fire properties.	1
3 Flexible PVC	Suitable for all domestic applications. More easily damaged by cigarette burns than alternatives.	1
4 Thermoplastic	Restrictive colour range compared with alternatives. Suitable for the majority of domestic applications; specifiers should confirm with manufacturers.	2

Health Comment	Rank	Cost Comment	Unit	Rate £s	Quantity per dwelling	Total cost per dwelling £s
Possibility of vinyl chloride monomer release. Hazard slight even for large areas. Sealed but wear and aging will release fibre. Problem of disposal (see Section IV).	2/3/3	300 x 300 x 2.0 mm tiles to BS 3260 fixed with adhesive.	m²	5.00	37m² *	185.00
Possibility of vinyl chloride monomer release. Hazard slight even for large areas. Sealed but potential fibre release by contact wear and aging.	0/1/1	300 x 300 x 2.0 mm tiles to BS 3260 fixed with adhesive.	m²	6.50	37m² *	240.50
Possibility of vinyl chloride monomer release. Hazard slight even for large areas.	0/0/0	300 x 300 x 2.0 mm tiles fixed with adhesive	m²	6.75	37m² *	249.75
May contain asbestos fibre which although sealed can release fibre with wear and aging.	2/3/3	300 x 300 x 2.0 mm tiles fixed with adhesive.	m²	5.00	37m² *	185.00

* Measured to ground floor only.

Application 7.22
TEXTURED PAINT COATINGS

Typical Situation

Technical Requirements

Various textured effects using viscous paints on plasterboard and plaster backgrounds. Must be crack free and resist cracking due to movement in backing. Ability to bond to other backgrounds an advantage. Should be water resistant and inhibit mould growth. Good fire properties, ie resistant to ignition and flame spread, an advantage. Easy removal also an advantage.

Decay and Degradation Factors

Decoration including sanding, recoating or simply repainting. Normal wear and tear. Possible surface condensation. Fire.

Guidance Notes

It is strongly recommended that asbestos-free coatings are used. From August 1984 the NHBC has prohibited the use of coatings containing asbestos fibre in properties covered by their warranty scheme. However, products incorporating asbestos are still available on the market although the largest manufacturer has discontinued its production.

Since certain subcontractors and applicators feel that there are practical and economic advantages in using coatings containing asbestos, supervisors and specifiers need to be vigilant in preventing substitution of asbestos material when asbestos free is required.

Existing coatings are not thought to present a serious hazard. overpainting with gloss paint would further reduce risk of fibre release. The main danger is likely to be caused by removal by dry abrasion (sanding down). This method should not be used. The best method is to use a proprietary hot wallpaper stripper or to soak with hot water to soften the coating and then scrape off. Scrapings should be disposed of properly — see Section IV.

Suspicion of substitution in the past exacerbates future problems of identification and therefore all coatings should be treated with caution when removal is considered.

Alternatives	Technical Comment	Rank
1 Coating containing 2 – 4 % asbestos fibre	Well-proven material of good workability giving quality finish. Good fire properties.	1
2 Asbestos-free types	Range of types and formulations, the main reason for choice depending on required finish. Suitability of coating depends on background on which it is to be applied. Therefore ranking variable. Available with varying fire properties.	Vari-able

Health Comment	Rank	Cost Comment	Unit	Rate £s	Quantity per dwelling	Total cost per dwelling £s
Sanding down for removal, maintenance or recoating; attrition and resin degradation may release fibres (see Section II .2)	3/3/3	Textured plastic coating to ceilings over 300 mm wide.	m^2	2.00	72m^2 *	144.00
If mineral fibre substitute, potential release and hazard will vary as material and fibre dimensions.	1/1/1	Textured plastic coating to ceilings over 300 mm wide.	m^2	2.00	72m^2 *	144.00

* Measured ceiling only.

Application 7.23
UNDERCOAT & FINISHING PAINT

Technical Requirements

Protective film applied to building materials to provide decorative effect. Generally applied as a liquid (may be thixotropic). Must have good bond to background — see Priming paint (Application 7.24). Good durability required in normal service within normal maintenance cycles (3–4 years). Ability to cope with movements in background essential. Wide range of colour pigments required. The combination of undercoat and finishing paint applied over the substrate may be required to have specified fire properties (ie resistance to flame spread).

Decay and Degradation Factors

Externally — natural weathering. Frost. Wild life. Internally — normal wear and tear. All locations — abrasion due to sanding down for recoating. Frequent contact with occupants to be expected.

Guidance Notes

Technical selection of paint systems is dependent upon the conditions of service of the film and compatibility with the primer. Specifiers are encouraged to adopt a systems approach, ie to use a manufacturers paint system for best results; however there is a problem where joinery is factory primed which may prevent complete adoption of this strategy. An additional primer coat is recommended in such circumstances.

From the health viewpoint the use of lead-free paint is recommended. This poses little problem on walls and ceilings as emulsion paints are lead free.

For joinery a number of lead-free solvent-based paints are available but the major difficulty for the specifier is distinguishing between these and the next category (low lead) as current requirements are such that labels need not provide information on lead content, when the paint contains less than 0.5% total lead.

The manufacturers, through their association, have made a commitment to change over completely to lead-free domestic paint formulations by 1987. In the meantime the Paintmakers' Association's advice is to contact individual manufacturers regarding the lead content of their paints. The editors have attempted this but the manufacturers have not co-operated. If our experience is representative of all enquiries the situation is plainly intolerable and could be easily overcome by the provision of the information on the tin and in trade literature.

Due to the problems encountered and to assist the reader a selection of the paints showing their lead content is produced in Appendix I.

So until all paints are lead free in 1987, those who wish to avoid all leaded paints have various alternatives open to them.
1. For internal applications, use two coats of acrylic primer/undercoat with a finishing coat of silk, vinyl emulsion which will give a semi-gloss finish.
2. For all applications select suitable paints from Appendix I (contact CLEAR or the London Boroughs of Islington who have carried out tests, for further information).
3. Use decorative stains for external applications — see Application 7.25. Care should be exercised when removing existing paint, especially in older property where high-lead paints may be suspected — see Section IV.

Alternatives	Technical Comment	Rank
1 Lead based: more than 5% (50 000 ppm) soluble lead, up to 30% (300 000 ppm) total lead	For external use. Slightly improved durability with lead-based paints giving longer period between maintenance, ie 4–5 years cycle.	1
2 Leaded: more than 1% (10 000 ppm) soluble lead but less than 5% (50 000 ppm) soluble lead	Little to choose between alternatives in terms of durability. Maintenance cycle 3–4 years. Reduction in lead content may extend drying period in adverse conditions.	1
3 Low lead: a. Less than 0.5% (5000 ppm) total lead b. Less than 0.25% (2500 ppm) total lead (toys standard)*		
4 Effectively lead free: less than 0.06% (600 ppm) (USA standard)		

* Paints made to toys standard intended for factory application. May not be suited to external applications on buildings.

Health Comment	Rank	Cost Comment	Unit	Rate £s	Quantity per dwelling	Total cost per dwelling £s
Significant hazard. Lead released by maintenance abrasion and decay. Hazard to infants by ingestion (see Section II 5.2).	3/3/3	No significant cost difference.				
Hazard diminishes in relation to reduction in lead content.	↓					
No hazard foreseen.	0/0/0					

Application 7.24
PRIMING PAINT

Technical Requirements

First coat in paint system. Primarily to provide key to surface for subsequent decorative coatings. Function of total paint film normally to provide protection and/or decoration to surface/material.

Decay and Degradation Factors

Externally — naturally weathering. Frost. Wild life. Internally — normal wear and tear. All locations — abrasion due to sanding down for recoating.

Guidance Notes

Technical selection of primer is dependent upon the material to be painted, the conditions of service and compatibility with subsequent finishing paints. Specifiers are encouraged to adopt a systems approach, ie to use a manufacturer's paint system for best results.

From a health viewpoint the use of lead-free paint is recommended. The comments on Application 7.23 apply here. This poses little problem with timber as a number of lead-free acrylic-based primers are available. Priming ferrous metals may pose something of a problem as traditional leaded primers have been used for their advantage of inhibiting corrosion. The use of low-lead zinc phosphate primer is advised. Designers might also consider going as far as the use of aluminium or stainless steel in locations where contact with infants is likely, so avoiding the need for corrosion inhibiting paints.

Removal of existing (leaded?) primers which may contain lead requires care — see Section IV.

Alternatives	Technical Comment	Rank
1 Lead based: more than 5 % (50 000 ppm) soluble lead, up to 50 % (500 000 ppm) total lead	For external use. Traditional lead-based primers, used on wood and ferrous metals, offering slightly improved durability.	1
2 Leaded: more than 1 % (10 000 ppm) soluble lead but less than 5 % (50 000 ppm) soluble lead	Little to choose between alternatives in terms of durability provided specifiers check compatibility with background material and subsequent finishing paints.	2
3 Low lead: less than 0.5 % (5000 ppm) total lead		
4 Effectively lead free: less than 0.06 % (600 ppm) (USA standard)		

Health Comment	Rank	Cost Comment	Unit	Rate £s	Quantity per dwelling	Total cost per dwelling £s
Significant hazard. Lead released by maintenance abrasion and decay. Hazard to infants by ingestion (see Section II 5.2).	3/3/3	No significant cost difference.				
Hazard diminishes in relation to reduction in lead content.						
No hazard foreseen.	0/0/0					

Application 7.25
VARNISH AND WOOD STAIN

Technical Requirements

Transparent protective film applied to timber and timber based products for decorative effect. Applied as a liquid. Must provide good bond to background. Good durability required in normal service within normal maintenance cycles (3—4 years). Ability to cope with movements in background essential. Colour pigments required.

Decay and Degradation Factors

Externally — natural weathering. Frost. Wild life. Internally — normal wear and tear. All locations — abrasion due to sanding and scraping down for recoating. Frequent contact with occupants to be expected.

Guidance Notes

This type of finish is selected primarily for appearance, ie so that the natural appearance of the timber is enhanced. Varnishes normally provide a clear impervious film which functions in a similar way to paint film in excluding moisture. Stains work on the principle of permitting the wood to breath, ie by not providing a completely impervious film. Many see this as a major technical advantage as the wood can dry out and does not remain waterlogged, which is possible with paints and varnishes once the film has been breached.

Lead-free varnishes are recommended on health grounds and comments on Application 7.23 apply here. Stains may contain fungicides and reference should be made to Application 7.26., Wood preservatives.

Care is required for the removal of existing leaded varnishes — see Section IV.

Alternatives	Technical Comment	Rank
1 Leaded: more than 1% (10 000 ppm) soluble lead but less than 5% (50 000 ppm) soluble lead	The lead content of clear varnish does not have a significant effect on the durability of the film, as this property depends on the other ingredients of the formulation.	
2 Low lead: less than 0.5% (5000 ppm) total lead		
3 Effectively lead free: less than 0.06% (600 ppm)		

Health Comment	Rank	Cost Comment	Unit	Rate £s	Quantity per dwelling	Total cost per dwelling £s
Lead released by maintenance, abrasion and decay. Hazard to infants by ingestion. Overall hazard diminishes in relation to reduction in lead content.	2/2/2	No significant cost difference.				
No hazard foreseen unless fungicides and insecticides present*. Then see Application 7.26.	0/0/0					

* Stains usually contain fungicides and insecticides. Note comments on Application 7.26 Wood preservatives.

Application 7.26
TIMBER PRESERVATIVES

Typical Situation

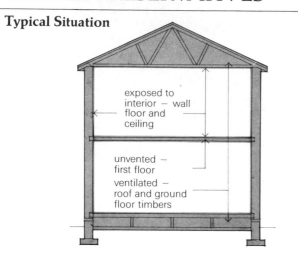

exposed to interior — wall floor and ceiling

unvented — first floor

ventilated — roof and ground floor timbers

Technical Requirements

Preservation by fungicidal and/or insecticidal action. Should be effective for life of building (ie 60 years) and remain in timber, resisting washing and leaching out for as long as possible. Must not increase combustibility of timber. Coloured dyes may be required to identify preserved timber or to supply decorative effect.

Decay and Degradation Factors

Fire. Evaporation of volatile chemicals. Abrasion from sanding down where decoration is expected. Frequent human contact inevitable with decorative wood stains, but restricted with structural timbers.

Guidance Notes

It should not be forgotten that these solutions are poisonous; however, properly applied in normal construction they are not thought to present any serious hazard. Variation in formulation between manufacturers products makes comment upon types difficult but from a health viewpoint the degree to which the preservative is fixed or locked in the timber is important. Volatile chemicals such as pentachlorophenol, lindane etc would appear in principle to offer slightly more hazard compared with the metal-based types, such as copper, chrome, arsenic solutions due to the tendency for the former to evaporate. The greatest hazard would occur during and shortly after application so that precautions must be taken to increase ventilation and reduce the occupants' exposure when remedial applications are undertaken in existing buildings.

In new buildings factory-treated timber would only cause concern when large quantities of timber are to be exposed within habitable rooms, eg if walls, ceilings and perhaps floors are all faced with treated timber and this is combined with low ventilation rates. Such circumstances are discussed in more detail in Section II 6.2.

Designers should therefore be conscious of the quantity of treated timber incorporated into new construction and the possible effect this may have on the indoor air quality. While it is usually necessary to treat the majority of structural timber to ensure durability, especially in timber framed construction, the need to treat decorative timber with volatile preservatives should be questioned.

It is also important to remind designers of the need for good constructional practice to reduce the risk of dampness and therefore of fungal attack. The use of preservatives in this circumstance should be seen as an extra precaution and not as the primary means of prevention.

Alternatives	Technical Comment	Rank
Active ingredients	Comments apply to all types	
1 Copper naphthenate	Various formulation combinations available from manufacturers.	
2 Zinc Naphthenate		
3 Copper/ chrome/ arsenic	Long-term effectiveness expected to be 30 years minimum but it is essential to confirm this with manufacturers.	
4 Tributyltin oxide	Solutions should comply with BS 4072 or BS 5707.	
5 Permethrin		
6 Pentachloro-phenol	Vacuum impregnation for new timbers generally considered superior to dipping, brush and spray application.	
7 Gamma-(Lindane)		
8 Dieldrin		

Selection must be related to timber species, location, method of application. Specialist advice should be sought from manufacturers.

Health Comment	Rank	Cost Comment	Unit	Rate £s	Quantity per dwelling	Total cost per dwelling £s
No hazard foreseen, with correct application.	0/0/0	No significant cost difference.				
Hazard due to possible evaporation of chemical over period of time. For small areas of treatment such as window frames. For large areas of treatment such as wall panelling, floors and ceilings. In well-ventilated areas such as roof space.	1/0/0 2/0/0 0/0/0					

Application 7.27

COLD WATER SUPPLY PIPEWORK

Typical Situation

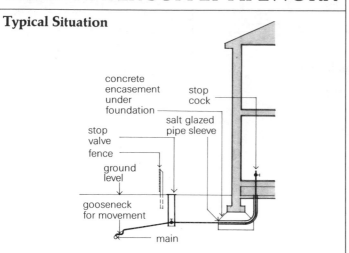

concrete
encasement
under
foundation
stop
cock

salt glazed
pipe sleeve
stop
valve
fence

ground
level

gooseneck
for movement

main

Technical Requirements

Impervious durable pipe system to connect from water mains to consumer's stop cock within the dwelling without contamination of supply water.

Essential that material must have good resistance to attack from ground water. Must not be crushed by overburden particularly when drained. Normally laid below frost line.

Decay and Degradation Factors

Attack from ground water which may contain a wide range of aggressive chemical compounds — especially when site redeveloped from tip or industrial usage. Possible frost action at access points.

Guidance Notes

The industry has moved away from metal tubing to various plastic alternatives for this application as some of the latter are available in long lengths thus drastically reducing the number of joints and therefore increasing the speed and convenience of installation.

Generally alternative 3 is most widely used and has a proven record.

Designers and specifiers should confirm with the manufacturer that Water Research Centre approval has been obtained for the product.

Lead supply pipework including mains distribution pipes were common in older property. When major alterations or refurbishment is contemplated it is advisable and may prove convenient to replace lead pipework while work is in progress. Otherwise the advice of the local environmental health officer should be sought in respect of the local water quality to ascertain whether immediate action should be taken to replace existing lead pipe.

Alternatives	Technical Comment	Rank
1 Copper	Well-proved material.	1
2 Stainless steel	More difficult to work than copper. Needs special flux containing phosphoric acid for soft solder capillary fittings.	1
3 Polythene (polyethylene)	Uses compression fittings. Flexible and available in long lengths.	1
4 Polyvinyl chloride (PVC)	Solvent weld fittings. Rigid material available in 6 m lengths.	1
5 Chlorinated PVC	Solvent weld fittings. Rigid material available in 6 m lengths.	1
6 Acrylonitrile butadiene styrene (ABS)	Solvent weld fittings. Rigid material available in 6 m lengths.	1
7 Lead	No longer specified.	—

Health Comment	Rank	Cost Comment	Unit	Rate £s	Quantity per dwelling	Total cost per dwelling £s
No significant hazard. See also Application 7.28 Fittings for copper pipes.	0/0/1	28 mm diameter copper tube to BS 2874 Table Y.	m	5.75	20 m *	115.00
No significant hazard.	0/1/0	28 mm diameter light gauge stainless steel tubing.	m	4.10	20 m *	82.00
No hazard foreseeable if pipes and fittings comply with BSI or Water Research Centre recommendations.	0/0/0	32 mm diameter polythene tube to BS 1972 Table 1 Class D.	m	4.20	20 m *	84.00
No hazard foreseeable if pipes and fittings comply with BSI or Water Research Centre recommendations.	0/0/0	32 mm uPVC tube to BS 3505 Class E.	m	4.30	20 m *	86.00
Lead free. No hazard foreseen if pipes and fittings comply with BSI or Water Research Centre recommendations.	0/0/0	28 mm CPVC tube.	m	4.00	20 m *	80.00
No hazard foreseeable if pipes and fittings comply with BSI or Water Research Centre recommendations.	0/0/0	32 mm diameter ABS tubing.	m	3.85	20 m *	77.00
Not recommended. Major hazard in soft water areas.	3/3/3	No longer specified.	—	—	—	—

* Nominal measurement only.

Application 7.28
FITTINGS FOR COPPER PIPE

Typical Situation

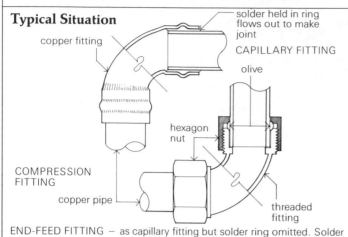

 END-FEED FITTING — as capillary fitting but solder ring omitted. Solder added by plumber.

Technical Requirements

Effective water-tight means of connecting copper pipe in plumbing systems. Essential that smooth bore at an even diameter is maintained through the joint which should have strength similar to pipe.

Decay and Degradation Factors

Corrosion and leaching of lead in system due to chemical properties of water eg bimetallic corrosion from weak acid solutions in water supply.

Guidance Notes

Here the major hazard is from lead solder used for fittings forming part of drinking water supply pipework where water is supplied from soft water areas (generally in Northern England, Wales and Scotland). Some excessively hard water areas may also be vulnerable to this problem but the chemical process resulting in the leaching of lead from the solder is different from that in soft water areas.

  Bearing this in mind alternatives 3 and 4 should be used for all cold water pipework and as stored water might be used for drinking (although this is not recommended — see Application 7.30) these alternatives must be considered for all hot and cold water systems.

  As the increase in cost of lead-free fittings for a typical dwelling is modest the authors have taken the view that the use of lead-free fittings throughout will be more convenient to specifiers than the cost in time spent contacting the environmental health office to ascertain the properties of the local water supply.

  End feed joints can be made using tin, silver solder, but cost may rise due to possible excessive use of solder by tradesmen.

  Alternatives 1 and 2 are satisfactory for other applications, eg sealed central heating systems. Close supervision would be necessary to prevent errors of identification particularly between lead solder and silver solder capillary fittings and as close supervision is difficult to guarantee it is suggested that all fittings used ought to be type 3 or 4.

  Where pipework is exposed the visual appearance of alternatives 1, 2 and 3 are usually preferred.

Alternatives	Technical Comment	Rank
1 End feed — lead solder	Effective method of jointing. Slight disadvantage in time taken to make joint.	1
2 Capillary — lead solder	Little to choose between these two now that tin, silver solder is available with similar melt temperature to lead with appropriate flux.	1
3 Capillary — tin, silver solder		1
4 Compression (Brass body with copper or brass olives)	Less satisfactory appearance. Fitting can be dismantled and reassembled with new olives.	1

Health Comment	Rank	Cost Comment	Unit	Rate £s	Quantity per dwelling	Total cost per dwelling £s
Potential hazard of solder in contact with water system mainly in soft water areas. Greater risk due to possibility of excess solder deposition within pipe.	3/2/3	15 mm, 22 mm, 28 mm elbows, tees, bends etc.	No	2.20	200 No	440.00
Potential hazard of solder in contact with water system mainly in soft water areas.	3/2/3	15 mm, 22mm, 28 mm elbows, tees, bends, etc.	No	2.00	200 No	400.00
Solder contains 0.1% lead, minimum hazard, acceptable as an alternative for lead.	1/0/1	15 mm, 22mm, 28 mm elbows, tees, bends, etc.	No	2.15	200 No	430.00
No hazard foreseen.	0/0/0	15 mm, 22mm, 28 mm elbows, tees, bends, etc.	No	2.40	200 No	480.00

Application 7.29
PIPE INSULATION

Typical Situation

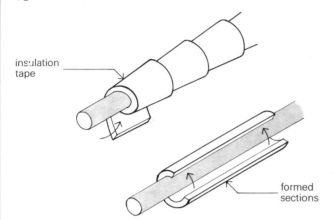

insulation tape

formed sections

Technical Requirements

Hot and cold water supply To provide sufficient insulation to prevent freezing of water in pipework in roof and other exposed locations.
Central heating pipework Reduce heat loss from pipework throughout dwelling and prevent frost damage when system out of use.
Both types Water resistant and rot-proof material essential. Good fire properties (ie resistance to ignition from small sources and resistance to flame spread) an advantage.

Decay and Degradation Factors

Wild life. Fire. Mainly concealed in ducts, floor and roof spaces, but may be exposed to the interior. Contamination of water supply via uncovered water storage tank by dust particles and fibres.

Guidance Notes

All types shown are satisfactory but alternatives 2—5 are preferred for central heating pipes due to combination of additional thickness and ease of application in confined spaces. Choice really depends upon cost factors plus additional consideration of appearance if insulation is to be exposed to interior spaces. In this circumstance consideration might also be given to the slight fire, toxic fume hazard of the plastic types 3, 4, 5 in the event of a fire. This would only be a problem if a significant amount of material is to be fitted in an exposed position. Otherwise the fire problem is further reduced where pipes are fixed in the usual position in roof, floor and duct spaces.

Combustible materials are obviously susceptible to ignition and care is required during plumbing operations which might involve the use of hot work with a naked flame (soldering, brazing, etc.)

Asbestos fibre/magnesia lagging composition was commonly used for insulation of heating systems in industrial and commercial buildings up to the late 1960s. The material was most suited to larger diameter pipes, heating and ventilating ducting and therefore found little application in normal domestic situations. However, larger houses and blocks of flats may well have the heating installation insulated with asbestos lagging. This material is potentially very dangerous and if suspected, guidance should be sought from the local environmental health officer regarding detailed identification and possible removal or sealing — see Section IV.

Alternatives	Technical Comment	Rank
1 Mineral wool band	Awkward to fix in confined spaces. Normally only used in concealed locations for frost protection. Good fire properties. Some varieties non-combustible.	2
2 Mineral wool formed sections	Formed sections usually thicker than mineral wool band therefore greater level of insulation. Good fire properties. Some varieties non-combustible.	1
3 Polystyrene formed sections	Combustible, available with various fire properties.	1
4 Isocyanurate formed sections	Combustible, available with various fire properties.	1
5 Foamed rubber formed sections	Usually complete tube permitting convenient fixing on new work. Combustible, available with various properties.	1
6 Asbestos lagging	No longer used in new work.	—

Health Comment	Rank	Cost Comment	Unit	Rate £s	Quantity per dwelling	Total cost per dwelling £s
Minimal risk of fibre release except during maintenance and DIY, provided pipes located in floors, roofs and ducts.	0/1/1	100 mm wide wrapping to 22 mm diameter pipe.	m	1.75	15 m	26.25
Minimal risk of fibre release except during maintenance and DIY, provided pipes located in floors, roofs and ducts. Fibre release reduced due to bonded nature of formed section.	0/0/1	19 mm thick around 22 mm diameter pipe.	m	2.75	15 m	41.25
No health risk foreseen except minimal hazard from toxic fumes in event of fire	0/1/0	19 mm thick around 22 mm diameter pipe.	m	2.25	15 m	33.75
No health risk foreseen except minimal hazard from toxic fumes in event of fire.	0/1/0	19 mm thick around 22 mm diameter pipe.	m	2.50	15 m	37.50
No health risk foreseen except minimal hazard from toxic fumes in event of fire.	0/1/0	19 mm thick around 22 mm diameter pipe.	m	2.50	15 m	37.50
Significant hazard. See Section IV.	3/3/3	No longer used in new work.	—	—	—	—

Application 7.30
COLD WATER STORAGE TANKS

Typical Situation

insulation — see Application 7.31

cover

tank

bearers

roof timbers

ceiling

Technical Requirements

Container for water storage must provide flexibility/ability to cut for feed and outflow pipes/valves etc. Cover essential. Self supporting over bearers an advantage. Material of tank should not contaminate water supply.

Decay and Degradation Factors

Danger might result from plumbing alterations where fibres are left in tank from cutting holes. Removal of lid for maintenance. Possible attack of material by aggressive waters causing release of particles and fibres. Build-up of sediment and corrosion may exacerbate this.

Guidance Notes

The main problem with this application is the view taken of the use of stored water for drinking purposes. The authors have considered the worst position, ie people will continue to use stored water although it is *strongly* recommended they should *not* do so. With this point in mind it is essential that installations are completed by a close fitting but not airtight lid to reduce contamination of stored water.

Asbestos cement tanks are not recommended on general environmental grounds. The effect on the health from ingestion of asbestos fibres is still the subject of research so it is not possible to give firm advice on the hazards existing from the use of asbestos cement tanks.

Replacement would seem advisable if the interior surface of the tanks appears friable, if there is obvious decay of the cement matrix or if alteration to the plumbing is contemplated requiring changes to the pipe connections to the tank. Old tanks should be disposed of properly — see Section IV.

Plastic pipes and tanks are obviously susceptible to ignition and care is required during plumbing operations which might involve the use of hot work with a naked flame (soldering, brazing, etc).

Otherwise the choice is dependent upon cost/convenience factors (ie shape/size of tank, position in roof, etc) although 'plastics' types, alternatives 2, 3 and 4 are now most common.

Alternatives	Technical Comment	Rank
1 Galvanized mild steel	Self supporting over bearers. Galvanized coating eventually broken down leading to corrosion.	2
2 Glass reinforced plastic (GRP)	Require full boarded base for support. Plastic types easier to cut for pipework.	1
3 Polythene	Require full boarded base for support. Plastic types easier to cut for pipework.	1
4 Polypropylene	Require full boarded base for support. Plastic types easier to cut for pipework.	1
5 Asbestos cement	Self supporting over bearers (not now manufactured)	1

Health Comment	Rank	Cost Comment	Unit	Rate £s	Quantity per dwelling	Total cost per dwelling £s
Slight disposal problem due to zinc content of coating, otherwise no hazard foreseen.	0/0/1	114 litre capacity tank including lid and placing in position.	No	60.00	1 No	60.00
Potentially a slight risk of release of fibres and plastic by leaching or maintenance work to water supply. No hazard foreseeable if tanks comply with BSI or Water Research Centre recommendations.	0/0/0	114 litre capacity tank including lid and placing in position.	No	50.00	1 No	50.00
No hazard foreseeable if tanks comply with BSI or Water Research Centre recommendations.	0/0/0	114 litre capacity tank including lid and placing in position.	No	43.00	1 No	43.00
No hazard foreseeable if tanks comply with BSI or Water Research Centre recommendations.	0/0/0	114 litre capacity standard (grey) tank including lid and placing in position	No	40.00	1 No	40.00
		114 litre capacity black tank including lid and placing in position.	No	43.00	1 No	43.00
Fibre release into water by maintenance work or possible leaching. Long-term effect unknown with current state of knowledge.	1/2/3	Not available.	—	—	—	—

Application 7.31

HOT & COLD WATER TANK INSULATION

Typical Situation

cylinder jacket encased in polythene bag

rigid board insulation

box filled with loose insulation

Technical Requirements

Hot water cylinders — reduce heat loss. Cold water storage tanks — prevent freezing. Both applications: water resistant, rot-proof material essential. Dimensionable stability an advantage. Good fire properties (ie resistance to ignition, non-combustibility) an advantage.

Decay and Degradation Factors

Wild life in roof space. Fire. Easily accessible in airing cupboards where long-term contact with occupants' clothing is likely. Contamination of water supply via uncovered water storage tanks by dust particles and fibres. See Appplications 7.8, 7.30.

Guidance Notes

When the hot cylinder is fitted in the usual position in an airing cupboard the standard mineral wool jacket or pre-foamed polyurethane lagged cylinder have the main advantage of ease of fitting.

For cold water tanks board types of insulation are generally easier to fit, but there may be problem locations where loose fill might prove most suitable. Final choice depends on the shape of tank and its location.

It is essential that open tanks have a close fitting (not sealed) lid to reduce contamination of stored water as this water may be used for drinking — see comments on Application 7.30. Board type insulation *should not* be used as the only covering to open tanks.

Caution should also be exercised with loose fill vermiculite due to the potential risk of 'asbestiform' fibre content — see Application 7.8.

Combustible materials are obviously susceptible to ignition and care is required during plumbing operations which might involve the use of hot work with a naked flame (soldering, brazing, etc.)

Alternatives	Technical Comment	Rank
1 Mineral wool jackets	Easy to fix. Non-combustible insulation encased in combustible jacket. Intended for hot water cylinders.	1
2 Mineral wool quilt	Non-combustible. Assessment assumes roof space application.	1
3 Mineral fibre board	Very easy to cut and fix around rectangular tank. Non-combustible.	1
4 Polystyrene beads	Loose insulation requiring boxing-in around tank and/or cylinder. Combustible, available with various fire properties.	2
5 Polystyrene board	Very easy to cut and fix around rectangular tank. Combustible, available with various fire properties.	1
6 Polyurethane chips	Loose insulation requiring boxing-in around tank and/or cylinder. Combustible, available with various fire properties.	2
7 Polyurethane board	Very easy to cut and fix around rectangular tank. Combustible, available with various fire properties.	1
8 Isocyanurate board	Very easy to cut and fix around rectangular tank. Combustible, available with various fire properties.	1
9 Vermiculite	Loose insulation requiring boxing-in around tank and/or cylinder. Greater thickness required for equivalent standard of insulation. Non-combustible.	2
10 Factory pre-formed polystyrene/ polyurethane foam attached to tank (hot water only)	Very convenient for new applications. Combustible, available with various fire properties.	1

Health Comment	Rank	Cost Comment	Unit	Rate £s	Quantity per dwelling	Total cost per dwelling £s
Slight risk of exposure if cylinder accessible. Loss of fibre reduced by plastic jacket.	0/1/1	50 mm thick jacket covered with polythene and complete with fixing bands to 114 litre cylinder (hot water only).	No	13.50	1 No	13.50
Cold water tank should be covered to minimize fibre contamination of the water supply. Slight risk of exposure if tanks are accessible. Rating 1/1/1 if exposed in airing cupboards.	0/1/1	100 mm thick quilt insulation.	No	15.00	2 No	30.00
Cold water tank should be covered to minimize fibre release to the water supply. Slight risk of exposure if tanks are accessible but material less friable than quilts.	0/1/1	25 mm thick board insulation.	No	12.00	2 No	24.00
No health risk foreseen except in event of fire.	0/2/0	100 mm thick loose insulation, (excluding boxing).	No	6.00	2 No	12.00
No health risk foreseen, except in event of fire.	0/2/0	75 mm thick board insulation.	No	12.50	2 No	25.00
Slight risk of sensitization. Additional health hazard if involved in fire.	1/2/0	100 mm thick loose insulation, (excluding boxing).	No	6.00	2 No	12.00
Slight risk of sensitization. Additional health hazard if involved in fire.	1/2/0	75 mm thick board insulation.	No	13.00	2 No	26.00
Slight sensitization risk. Additional health hazard if involved in fire.	1/2/0	25 mm thick board insulation.	No	13.50	2 No	27.00
If asbestiform fibrous dust involved then hazardous. If it can be shown after examination using electron microscopy there are no such fibres the rating would be 0/0/0.	3/3/3	100 mm thick loose insulation, (excluding boxing).	No	8.00	2 No	16.00
Slight risk of sensitization. Additional health hazard if involved in fire.	1/2/0	Factory pre-formed polyurethane foam attached to 114 litre cylinder (hot water only).	No	18.00	1 No	18.00

Application 7.32

CENTRAL HEATING BOILER INSULATION

Typical Situation

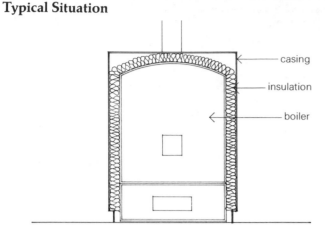

casing

insulation

boiler

Technical Requirements

Non-combustible insulating jacket to reduce heat loss from boiler and reduce outer casing to safe temperature. Water resistant and rot-proof material essential.

Noise absorbing properties an advantage.

Decay and Degradation Factors

Contact with occupants should only occur when casing removed for maintenance.

Guidance Notes

Due to the requirement for non-combustible material, mineral wool in one of the three forms shown (normally board or foil faced quilt), is now the usual choice made by boiler manufacturers.

The main hazard stems from existing boilers lagged with asbestos fibre based insulation. Very few domestic boilers are thought to be lagged with this material as it was generally applied only to larger boiler installations. However, boilers installed before the late 1960s particularly free-standing, uncased, sectional types might be insulated with asbestos fibre material. It would therefore seem essential to check all boilers installed before 1969 to ascertain the type of insulation, especially if removal or disposal is contemplated — see Section IV.

Caution should also be exercised with loose fill vermiculite due to the risk of 'asbestiform' fibre content — see Application 7.8. However, when mixed in a cement matrix and in position surrounding a back boiler the hazard to the occupier would be negligible.

Alternatives	Technical Comment	Rank
1 Loose mineral fibre	Choice depends on design and size of boiler.	
2 Mineral fibre quilt		1
3 Mineral fibre board		1
4 Vermiculite	Used mainly for back boiler installations to solid fuel appliances in 1 part cement to 6 parts vermiculite mix.	1
5 Asbestos lagging	No longer used in new work.	—

Health Comment	Rank	Cost Comment	Unit	Rate £s	Quantity per dwelling	Total cost per dwelling £'s
Slight exposure to fibres during maintenance only.	0/1/1	No significant effect on boiler cost.				
	0/0/1					
	0/0/1					
If asbestiform fibrous dust involved then hazardous if disturbed by alterations and maintenance. If it can be shown after examination using electron microscopy there are no fibres the rating would be 0/0/0.	0/3/3					
Significant hazard. See guidance notes.	3/3/3					

Application 7.33
FLUE PIPES

Typical Situation

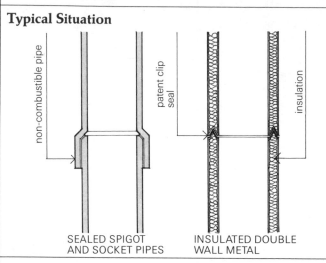

SEALED SPIGOT AND SOCKET PIPES   INSULATED DOUBLE WALL METAL

Technical Requirements

Sealed non-combustible pipe to vent combustion gases to external air. Effective joint seals are absolutely essential. Span between recommended fixing centres. Adequate isolation from combustible structure. Resistance to chemical attack from combustion product and condensate to give adequate life. Must be durable and frost resistant where exposed externally.

Decay and Degradation Factors

External application — natural weathering. Frost, attack by wild life.
Internal application — possible decoration, normal wear and tear.
Interior of flue — attack by combustion and condensate.

Guidance Notes

Generally stainless steel types are selected for internal applications where appearance is important.

    Use of exposed asbestos cement should be discontinued on general environmental grounds. Avoid rubbing down asbestos flues for cleaning and decoration. Consideration could also be given to enclosing existing flues in metal casing to reduce potential fibre release due to natural weathering. Asbestos cement pipe and asbestos filled metal type should be disposed of carefully at renewal — see Section IV.

    From a health viewpoint normal masonry flues could be considered provided the designer can be sure that flues will remain gas tight in service. Escape of flue gases could form a more serious hazard than that posed by the construction materials.

Alternatives	Technical Comment	Rank
1 Asbestos cement	Proven material in this application but poor appearance. Generally fitted in duct or external to the building.	1
2 Masonry	Traditional method of flue construction utilizing sectional linings requiring good workmanship for effective seal.	1
3 Double wall stainless steel	Generally convenient to fix. Better appearance than asbestos cement so generally preferred when visible.	
(a) Asbestos filled		1
(b) Mineral fibre filled		1
4 Double Wall with galvanized steel outer wall and aluminium inner wall — air filled	Generally convenient to fix. Better appearance than asbestos cement. Normally used for gas and oil fired appliances. May not be suitable for solid fuel.	2

Health Comment	Rank	Cost Comment	Unit	Rate £s	Quantity per dwelling	Total cost per dwelling £s
Damage through wear, aging and maintenance may release fibre. Potential hazard from cleaning exposed and internal flues. Disposal problem (see Section IV).	1/3/3	150 mm diameter pipe.	m	47.50	2 m	95.00
No hazard foreseen.	0/0/0	Precast block flue 231 mm x 65 mm aperture.	m	20.00	2 m	40.00
No metals hazard.		150 mm diameter insulated double wall stainless steel pipe.				
Sealed in casing. Physical contact remote. No problem provided correct maintenance does not release fibre.	0/3/3	(a) asbestos filled	m	100.00	2 m	200.00
Sealed in casing. Physical contact remote. No problem provided correct maintenance does not release fibre.	0/1/1	(b) baked rockwool	m	115.00	2 m	230.00
No hazard foreseen.	0/0/0	150 mm diameter pipe.	m	60.00	2 m	120.00

SECTION IV

HAZARDOUS MATERIALS IN EXISTING BUILDINGS

8 Hazardous materials in existing buildings

S. R. CURWELL, BSc MSc ARIBA
C. G. MARCH, BSc MCIOB

8.1 Introduction

Applications of materials which although no longer available or permitted can still be found in existing buildings have been included in the comparisons made on the data sheets included in Section III. The purpose of this section is to expand on this and provide general information, comment and advice on whether to remove existing hazardous materials, and if so how to carry out this operation and eventually dispose of the offending material. The prime causes for concern are the majority of asbestos applications and lead used in water supply installations and also in paintwork.

At the end of each section can be found a list of names and addresses where up to date information can be sought.

The procedures are given only in outline as this section is supplementary to the main theme of the text dealing with the selection of materials. Also individual local authorities may have their own requirements and codes of practice.

8.2 Asbestos

8.2.1 Validity of removal

There are obvious cases where asbestos should be removed because there is an established risk to the health of the occupants of the buildings: in circumstances where fibre is being released into the atmosphere due to degradation of the material by abrasion, decay and similar factors and where no reasonable amount of repair will stop this from occurring. On the other hand, materials containing asbestos fibre are used in applications where the material is completely contained, for example when encased inside a double-walled stainless-steel flue, where the likelihood of fibre release in normal use is virtually nil.

So, the question arises, should the material be removed or left alone if it is not subject to damage, or if this has occurred and further damage is not to be expected, should it be repaired or replaced? This is the problem the building owner, manager, designer, surveyor or contractor concerned must address.

Some would take the view that a total ban and thus immediate removal approach must be applied on the argument that 'it only takes one asbestos fibre to cause asbestos related diseases', but most would be more liberal in their interpretation of the level of risk. Indeed the irresponsible or incorrect removal of the material could be more hazardous, particularly to the operatives and occupants, than leaving well alone or in the case of damaged material taking appropriate protective remedial measures.

It is therefore impossible to make this judgement on behalf of others in this area of doubt. One's own personal perception of risk coupled with that of the client and occupiers and their respective objectives must influence the course of action, which may mean that a decision to remove can be based on emotive reasoning rather than an objective consideration of the hard facts as they are presented. Nor should the sometimes enormous costs of removal be underated or the difficulty in complete removal of the material which can lodge in voids and cavities.

8.2.2 Identification and sampling of asbestos

The most likely places where asbestos may be found in low-rise residential buildings have been identified on the data sheets in Section III. It should be noted that over the lifetime of the building there is a possibility that asbestos fibre may have been released due to previous alteration and decoration. Therefore fibres could have spread around the building into places other than where originally installed.

However, the asbestos materials may have been painted over or otherwise concealed, thus disguising its true nature and, even if this is not the case, many of the substitute materials have a similar appearance even to the experienced eye. Even if it has been established that the material contains asbestos fibre, it will probably still not be known whether the fibre is white, blue or brown. To be sure, bulk and air samples will have to be taken by a qualified person and taken away for analysis. The Environmental Health Department of the local authority should be contacted if there is any doubt at all. They will provide, or advise on, a sampling and analysis service. The following notes provide only an outline of the general procedure. Readers *must not* attempt to carry out sampling and removal procedures without seeking proper advice from the local authority health department or health and safety executive or suitably qualified laboratory.

Further information can also be obtained from the Asbestos Information Centre, Sackville House, 40 Piccadilly, London W1V 9PA, funded by the Fibre Cement Manufacturers Association.

Advice on the procedures and precautions to be taken are outlined in the Health and Safety Executive Code of Practice: Work with Asbestos Insulation and Coating (1983) and Guidance Notes EH36: Work with Asbestos Cement or EH37: Work with Asbestos Insulation Board (both dated October 1984).

The vast majority of asbestos applications in domestic buildings will involve asbestos cement and insulation board. The points from these publications are abstracted below. (Crown copyright — reproduced with the permission of the Controller of Her Majesty's Stationery Office.)

Whenever it is necessary to work on or disturb a material containing asbestos fibre its composition should first be determined so that any necessary precautions can be taken before the work is started. The presence of asbestos may be indicated on original building plans or specifications. Information about the presence and type of asbestos may also be available from the architect or builder who constructed the building, or from the original supplier of the insulation board or cement product if known. A voluntary labelling scheme was introduced for asbestos products in 1976 using an 'a' logo to indicate the presence of asbestos. However, very little asbestos insulating board or cement products found in existing buildings is likely to bear this label.

If in doubt, the only satisfactory way of determining if asbestos is present in cement is by bulk sampling and laboratory analysis. But even the sampling operation can put people at risk so it should only be done when the above alternatives have been tried and when there is a specific need to confirm the presence of asbestos. Sampling should only be carried out by someone with suitable training and experience. Once asbestos has been identified, records should be made and kept available for any future work activity.

As insulation boards and cement products will normally be of uniform composition, there should in most cases be little difficulty in selecting a site for sampling which is not only representative but also readily accessible and, importantly, can be easily cleaned and repaired after sampling. Asbestos insulating board may, however, have been repaired or extended with non-asbestos materials; it is therefore important to examine all material for changes in characteristics or modifications/repair which may indicate a different composition and to ensure that samples are taken from all the types of material present.* Removal of samples must not compromise any fire resisting properties of the structure.

Sampling techniques used should minimise the release of fibre and cause the minimum disturbance to the rest of the installation. This is particularly important when working overhead.

Where old asbestos cement is involved, it is important to confirm the fibre type by sampling and analysis so that appropriate precautions can be taken.

The Health and Safety Executive (HSE) must be given 28 days notice before any work can start on materials containing crocidolite (blue asbestos). If there is any doubt of the type of asbestos, then it should be assumed that it is blue asbestos and HSE should be notified.

It should be noted that the licenced contractors must give 28 days notice to the HSE irrespective of the type of fibre as a condition of their licence.

8.2.3 Precautions when taking bulk samples of the material

(a) *Asbestos cement products*

1.   Ensure a safe means of access if working at heights (e.g. on roof or wall cladding).
2.   Only the people doing the sampling should be in the immediate area.
3.   Take care to minimise damage to the asbestos cement from which the sample is taken. Use a small hand tool and place the sample in a suitably labelled small sealable container (e.g. self-sealing polythene bag: it is good practice to double bag, i.e. one bag within another).
4.   Clean any surfaces contaminated during sampling. Use a dustless method such as a damp cloth which should be disposed of in a labelled, sealed container while still damp. If extensive contamination is likely, particularly indoors, use a suitable vacuum cleaner with a high-efficiency filter (constructed to BS 5415 Appendix C Type 4). Where furnishings may be contaminated, or if cleaning dust and debris is a problem, cover the threatened surfaces with an impervious sheet.
5.   Seal any surfaces damaged when the sample is taken to limit the possibility of fibre release.

(b) *Asbestos insulation board*

1.   If the work involves cutting, boring, drilling etc. or if the board is friable, suitable approved respiratory equipment and protective clothing should be provided and worn.
2.   No other person should be in the immediate vicinity of the work.
3.   Wherever possible, the area of insulating board to be sampled should be thoroughly wetted§.
4.   The sample should be taken using a hand tool (e.g. knife, cork borer or hand drill) and placed in a small sealable container (e.g. self-sealing polythene bag or stoppered bottle) which should be suitably labelled.
5.   Surfaces onto which dust/debris may fall should be covered with an impervious sheet before the sample is taken (unless the surface itself is impervious), and should be cleaned afterwards by a dustless method such as a suitable vacuum cleaner with a high-efficiency filter or a damp cloth which should be disposed of in a sealed bag whilst still damp.

*It is not sufficient merely to sample dust deposits in the vicinity of the material.
§Appropriate precautions must be taken to protect or isolate electrical equipment and installations.

6.   The hole or newly exposed surface should be treated with a suitable sealant which does not adversely affect the fire protection or structural integrity of the material.

In addition to bulk samples, it may be necessary to take dust samples from undisturbed areas in the general vicinity.

8.2.3 Air monitoring and control limits

If the asbestos-containing material has been damaged or there is suspicion that fibres are being released, then it is necessary to measure the amount of asbestos fibre in the air by taking air samples. This is done by drawing air through a filter at a given rate over a fixed period of time and then determining the number of fibres that have been collected on the filter using a microscope. Again the local environmental health department will carry out this work or advise of an organization equipped to do such work.

The Asbestosis Research Council have produced technical notes numbers 1, 2 and 3 entitled 'The measurement of airborne asbestos dust by the membrane filter method', 'Dust sampling procedures for use with the asbestos regulations' and 'Recommendations for the sampling and identification of asbestos in asbestos products', respectively. The HSE Guidance note EH10 also gives detailed information on the measurement of airborne dust concentrations and the assessment of control measures. The assessment of results of these procedures forms the most difficult problem.

The current control limits for occupational exposure are:

(a)   dust containing any crocidolite (blue) or amosite (brown) asbestos   0.2 fibres/ml
(b)   dust containing other types of asbestos but excluding crocidolite and
       amosite   0.5 fibres/ml

Both limits refer to a 4 hour reference period and fibre counting using an optical microscope. Electron microscopy is more effective in identifying the existence of fibres but as yet there is little or no means of relating fibre counts obtained by this method to statistics of incidence of disease. Cost of tests are of the order of £10 for optical methods and £200−300 using electron microscopy, excluding the cost of air sampling (12 air samples for optical microscopy are usually regarded as a minimum to give an effective analysis, but this number will depend upon individual circumstances).

As explained on page 17 Section II the current practice of downwards adjustment of the figures for occupational exposure to provide a 'safe' level for general environmental exposure is not appropriate. The main reasons for this are to do with the particular nature of the risks posed by asbestos fibre and the accuracy of air sampling and fibre counting procedures.

Nevertheless, as the control limits shown represent upper limits for occuational exposure, which it is asumed will be limited to the 40 hours of a working week, then in the event of air monitoring in a dwelling or similar building producing results approaching these levels there would be serious cause for concern. Any regular recording of fibres must be a risk to occupants.

8.2.6 Repairing damage to asbestos cement and insulating board

If it is decided that a sealing operation is appropriate the following steps as outlined in the Department of the Environment publication Asbestos materials in Building (1983) should be utilized.

Rigid asbestos materials such as insulating board or asbestos-cement may be sealed by painting. The surface should be prepared using chemical cleansers and damaged areas repaired, with a substitute material. Asbestos materials should not be sanded or wire-brushed. Dusty surfaces can be cleaned with an industrial vacuum cleaner fitted with a high efficiency filter constructed to BS5415 Appendix C, Type H or wiped with a damp cloth which is disposed of while still damp in a sealed bag. Asbestos cement used externally may need treatment with a biocide to remove algae before painting.

The above procedure is for normal working, but it is permissible to use abrasive preparation techniques when a proper protective working enclosure is constructed, kept under negative pressure, and qualified operatives are protected with appropriate clothing and respiratory equipment. The extract air must be properly filtered to remove asbestos fibres.

Insulating board can be painted with an initial coat of diluted PVA emulsion followed by one or more full strength coats. Asbestos Cement is alkaline and should be primed with an alkali-resistant primer or a chlorinated rubber or oleo-resinous paint followed by one or more top coats. Where possible both sides should be painted.

When a higher degree of protection from damage is required a number of other sealing systems are available

  (i)   flexible or semiflexible polymeric or bitumen coating;

 (ii)   inorganic cement type coating;

(iii)   preformed sheet or panels.

The choice of sealing system depends on the nature of the asbestos material and its location, the degree of damage protection required and any surface flammability requirements.

In most circumstances it may prove advisable to remove friable (easily crumbled or pulverized) materials, such as sprayed asbestos which is unlikely to be found in domestic construction. In exceptional circumstances these materials can be sealed with sprayed or brushed polymeric or bituminous coatings or with a hard setting cement type coating supported, if necessary, by a metal mesh. The sealing coat must adhere firmly, and the asbestos material itself should be checked to ensure that it is sound and firmly attached to the underlying surface. Alternatively asbestos surfaces can be boxed-in with sheet material suitably sealed at corners and edges, provided adequate resistance to fire spread can be maintained. The enclosed areas between the covering and the asbestos material should be sealed and adequate cavity fire barriers constructed. In all cases precautions must be taken to protect the people doing the work from exposure to asbestos dust and those who may subsequently live in the building.

Where asbestos insulation is being used for fire protection it is important that the fire hazard is not increased by the use of combustible sealants. The sealed materials must meet the standard for spread of flame specified in the Building Regulations (as defined in BS 476). Normal paints may not achieve this standard and specially formulated sealants are available.

Arrangements should be made to alert maintenance workers to the existence of asbestos materials. The presence of asbestos should be marked on building records or plans, and as an additional precaution warning notices should be attached at places where the material might be disturbed during maintenance work. In the case of housing, occupants should be made aware of the location of any asbestos materials and advised of appropriate precautions. Sealed asbestos should be checked regularly to ensure that the sealing is intact.

8.2.5 Removal and disposal procedures

Removal is usually considered necessary for friable or damaged asbestos materials and is in itself a very hazardous procedure both to the occupants and the operatives. Unfortunately the restrictions and regulations placed upon the operatives have to be so stringent for their own safety that it is probable they take short cuts, thus endangering their own health. While not in the brief of this text it cannot be over stressed how important it is that operatives engaged in this work are properly supervised and controlled, not just for their own sake but for the safety of others using the premises after they have finished their work.

When it is necessary to remove asbestos containing materials it is essential that a properly qualified contractor is employed. Properly qualified meaning having experience and also being licenced to carry out this work. Currently the problem is that possession of a licence is no guarantee the work will be executed in a proper fashion. There are several 'cowboys' doing this work and they must never be used as they create an additional hazard to their own workmen and to the occupants and others in the vicinity. It should be noted that it is a requirement to use a licenced contractor to remove friable insulating material. Although the present situation is unsatisfactory, on balance a licenced contractor is more likely to be familiar with the problems of removal. It is not just a case of ensuring competent contractors are employed and supervised carrying out the removal it is also important that continuous monitoring by air sampling is carried out at the workplace and surrounding areas. The premises must be vacuumed out on completion using a machine equipped with a special high efficiency filter arrangement capable of removing the very fine respirable fibres from the atmosphere, constructed to BS 5415 Appendix (Type H). Suitable machines are Nilfisk GS81h and GS82h. *Ordinary domestic and industrial vacuum cleaners are completely inadequate.*

HSE Guidance Notes EH36 and 37 should be consulted. The main points are

(a)   Those not engaged in the activity should not be permitted in the vicinity of the work, and should preferably not remain the same room when the work is carried out. (If necessary, signs and barriers should be erected around the work position).

(b)   Those engaged in the work should wear suitable approved respiratory protective equipment. If the work can be carried out carefully and is of short duration, an orinasal respirator should suffice. If it is necessary to break the insulating board containing crocidolite or amosite, or cutting is to be carried out, then a higher efficiency respirator will be required.

(c)   Suitable overalls or protective clothing should be worn by those engaged in the work. If working overhead, this should include a hood or other head covering. If the overalls become contaminated by asbestos dust they should be sealed in an impervious container, suitably marked, and sent to be cleaned or disposed of.

(d)   Equipment etc. in the vicinity of the work should be removed or covered in an impervious sheet before work begins.

(e)   Working methods should be chosen carefully to minimize dust release. Hand tools should be used rather than machines, and boards should be carefully removed, not broken. Where possible, the insulating board should be wetted before work begins. If the board contains crocidolite or amosite, a little detergent should be added to the water. (Care should be taken to prevent the water and detergent from making the floor slippery).

(f)   On completion of the work, surfaces etc. should be thoroughly cleaned of dust and debris by a dustless method.

(g)   Washing and changing facilities should be provided and used. For small operations where contamination is minimal, it will be acceptable to use the normal facilities in a building (i.e. cloakrooms etc.) for the storage of clean clothing and for washing. Any contaminated protective clothing should not be taken outside the work area unless sealed in suitably labelled impervious container (e.g. plastic bag). If contamination of hands and arms is likely, a basin or bowl should be provided for washing adjacent to the work area. If bodily contamination and/or heavy contamination of protective clothing is likely, decontamination facilities should be provided and used.

When removal of a significant quantity of asbestos-containing materials is necessary the use of negative-pressure techniques with appropriate temporary enclosures form the most effective method of controlling and containing dust and fibre release into the general environment.

Equally, disposal procedures, both in the transportation to the tipping site and when placed in the tip must be controlled and carried out correctly or long-term environmental problems could ensue.

Any container used for the disposal of asbestos waste should be

(a)   made from an impermeable material;
(b)   strong enough to remain dust tight even under wet conditions; and
(c)   adequately labelled. Where crocidolite is present it should be boldly marked 'BLUE ASBESTOS — DO NOT INHALE DUST'. The markings should be durable and of a type which cannot become detached from its container.

When each container is filled

(a)   it should be sealed to prevent the escape of dust during handling, transportation and disposal;
(b)   its external surface should be cleaned; and
(c)   it should be removed from the immediate working area to await removal to an authorised tip.

A system should be set up to ensure that the individual containers awaiting removal to an authorised waste tip are kept in an area set aside for storage.

Detailed guidance on asbestos waste disposal is contained in the Department of the Environment Waste Management Paper No. 18 *Asbestos Wastes — A Technical Memorandum on Arisings and Disposal,* including a Code of Practice.

Asbestos waste should be disposed of only

(a)   at a waste disposal site licensed for the purpose by the appropriate waste disposal authority; and
(b)   in accordance with the requirements of that authority.

Again regulation for the removal and disposal can be updated. Currently draft regulations and code of practice for control of asbestos at work, which includes removal in the home, are going through the consultative process. The local Environmental Health Officer, the Health and Safety Executive, and the Asbestos Information Centre are able to provide the necessary updated information and advice. The Metropolitan Boroughs and County Councils are responsible for providing disposal facilities for toxic waste and will give details of appropriate sites.

It will be obvious after reading the previous sections on removal and disposal of asbestos containing products that the procedures entail considerable expense when carried out correctly. The comparative cost of sealing or removal will need careful consideration before a decision is made in any particular circumstance.

8.2.6 Essential References

For those likely to be engaged in the identification of and decision to remove asbestos, as a minimum it is recommended that they should have the following references at hand

'Asbestos materials in Buildings' by the Department of the Environment. HMSO 1983.
'Asbestos — control limits, measurement of airborne dust concentrations and the assessment of control measures'. Guidance note EH10 from the Health and Safety Executive. HMSO (revised July 1984).
'Work with Asbestos Insulation and Coating'. Code of Practice from the Health and Safety Executive HMSO (1983)

A Guide to the Asbestos (Licencing) Regulations, 1983, HS(R)19, HMSO.
'Work with asbestos cement'. Guidance note EH37 from the Health and Safety Executive.
    HMSO (October 1984).
'Work with asbestos insulation board'. Guidance note EH37 from the Health and Safety
    Executive. HMSO (October 1984).
'Asbestos'. Guidance note MS13 from the Health and Safety Executive. HMSO (January
    1980).
'Asbestos in the home'. Asbestos Information Centre (April 1983).
'Asbestos in building'. Asbestos Information Centre (February 1982).

If working in London then:

'Code of Practice for the Removal of Asbestos'. Greater London Council/Inner London
Education Authority (August 1984).

The Asbestos Information Centre (AIC) produce further information which may also be
of use depending upon the amount of involvement in asbestos identification and removal
that is envisaged. These are

Asbestos — its special attributes and uses
Asbestos related diseases (a guide to the GP)
Asbestos — advantages and alternatives
Asbestos — products labelling scheme
Asbestos in building
Asbestos waste disposal directory
Manufactures of vacuum units
Hirers of vacuum units
Suppliers of waste disposal sacks
Recommended sealants

Technical Notes:

No.1   The measurement of airborne asbestos dust by the membrane filter method
No.2   Dust sampling procedures for use with the asbestos regulations
No.3   Sampling and identification of asbestos in asbestos products

The AIC will also provide on request the following

1.   Laboratories offering services associated with the sampling, testing and air monitoring.
2.   Manufacturers of sealants recommended for the encapsulation of asbestos lagging
       and/or sprayed insulation.
3.   Suppliers of plastic sacks for disposal.
4.   Manufacturers/suppliers — protective clothing for work with asbestos.
5.   Companies willing to launder protective clothing used for work with asbestos.
6.   Manufacturers/suppliers of vacuum equipment for work with asbestos.
7.   Hirers of portable vacuum units.
8.   Companies able to supply approved labels.
9.   Companies with mobile decontamination units.

There is also a useful book by the publication section of Environmental Information and
Analysis (EIA) produced in 1982 entitled 'Asbestos in the urban environment — a manual
of control'.

8.3 Lead

8.3.1 Water supply [1]

Where lead pipework is known or suspected in existing buildings the action to be taken is dependent upon the plumbosolvency of the water. Contact with lead during distribution does not necessarily result in contamination of water. The physical and chemical characteristics of the water — for example acidity, hardness and temperature — determine its ability to dissolve lead. Soft, acid water generally shows the greatest plumbosolvency, though recently some hard alkaline waters have been found to be plumbosolvent, the reasons for this being not yet fully understood. The lead content of water at the tap depends on the particular combination of circumstances prevailing before and during each drawing of a sample. Given the number of variables involved — for example pipe length and condition, time for which water has been standing, and water flow rate — it is not surprising that the lead content of random samples taken at the same tap can vary considerably. Wide variations in the amount of water drunk and consumed indirectly by different people also make it difficult to estimate to what extent lead in tap water contributes to an average individual's total intake of lead, though it has been estimated that an adult's intake from tap water beverages and cooking water is usually about 10 μg/day*, and possibly 30 times this amount in an area where plumbosolvency is a problem. These main areas are the North of England, Wales and parts of Scotland although this by no means identifies every area of concern. Designers should contact the local water authority for detailed advice on local water quality.

It has been estimated that 45 % of households in Great Britain use water that has at some stage passed through lead pipework or tanks. Lead is found in the distribution system, in the domestic service branch pipes and also in pipework and storage system within the home, although by this date it is thought that the majority of storage tanks have now been replaced by necessary maintenance and improvement work.

Identification may pose a problem. Surface mounted pipe is obvious, but the real difficulty arises in trying to establish the nature of alterations during the life of the building. For example, what appears to be a copper supply pipe may simply be a short length of copper jointed to an otherwise lead pipe and subsequently concealed by a new floor slab. It would therefore be advisable for designers to investigate fully either by instigating an analysis of water quality or by excavation of existing pipework when alterations or refurbishment is contemplated. The local environmental health office can advise on the address of the public analysist or appropriate private laboratories who can carry out the analysis. In certain areas grants may be available for replacement work.

It should be noted that removal of lead water supply pipes in the house may not totally resolve the problem since the communication pipe, owned and serviced by the water authority, may also be of lead.

While replacement is the most positive method of removing the risks posed by lead pipework it may not always be necessary to do this immediately as some water authorities are investigating the effectiveness of treating water supplies to reduce plumbosolvency. In such circumstances replacement might be delayed until a convenient moment such as when a major overhaul of the plumbing system is required, when refurbishment of the property is in hand or when the property changes ownership. The water authority should be contacted for advice.

When replacement is contemplated advice on alternative materials is provided in Application sheets 7.27 and 7.28.

*The WHO maximum permitted concentration is 100 μg/day and the EEC 50 μg/day.

8.3.2 Paint[2]

Chemical analysis is required before one can say with any certainty whether or not a particular piece of paintwork has a significant lead content. But history gives a useful general guide. Before the First World War, lead-based paint was used very extensively on walls, wood and metal, both indoors and outdoors. All paintwork and priming thought to date from before the First World War is likely to contain significant amounts of lead. Technical changes after about 1920 caused steady reductions in both the average lead content of leaded paints and their use, first for indoor work, and later even for outdoor priming. So leaded paintwork is very likely to be found on the exteriors of inter-war buildings and is not uncommon on interior surfaces, especially in the priming coats. The overall reduction in lead content has continued and is expected to fall to a maximum of 600 ppm in all domestic decorative paints by July 1987. Thus there is still the possibility that unsuitable leaded paint or primer has been used. A small flake of paint is all that is needed for an inexpensive test to establish the lead content. It must also be borne in mind that: (a) recent unleaded paintwork may conceal older, lead-based paint or primer; and (b) older woodwork may have some leaded primer left on it after it has been stripped. Exterior metal work of whatever age is very likely to have at least a lead-based primer on it unless it has been stripped recently and deliberately repainted with low-lead paint and primer.

Leaded paintwork only becomes a serious hazard when it it disturbed, and then only if the disturbance is such that people breathe or eat dust or debris. Sound paintwork, free from peeling, cracking, chipping or other deterioration, poses no problem except in the case of children suffering from 'pica' see Section II.

Although children with pica do not always chew paint or painted surfaces, where a child has this condition the only completely reliable safety measure is to remove the child to a place which is known to be free from leaded paint, especially on accessible surfaces. Failing that, the child should be closely supervised and all accessible surfaces in the home should be stripped with care and repainted with low-lead paint, taking care to follow the precautions set out below.

Once lead paintwork is detected it does not necessarily follow that it needs to be removed. Wholesale removal is generally neither feasible nor cost-effective and, if not done with scrupulous care, will probably make matters worse by releasing lead dust and particles around the home to be inhaled and ingested. When paintwork is sound, and children are not exposed to it, it is unlikely to present any serious hazard, whatever its lead content, if it is left alone or simply covered with modern paint in the course of normal redecoration. Preparation of sound paintwork should be restricted to cleaning using ordinary domestic cleaning solutions and very light surface abrasion using 'wet and dry' paper in order to scratch the surface and give a key for the following coats. However, there may eventually come a time when the paint will of necessity need to be stripped off due to decay or at major refurbishment.

Where leaded paint is flaking or crumbling, or needs to be removed for some other reason, there are a number of precautions which should be taken by both professional and amateur decorators[3]. Dry-sanding, whether for surface preparation or complete removal of the paint, is hazardous, particularly when power tools are used. The large quantities of dust released may be directly breathed in and contribute to high indoor lead concentrations for extended periods. The hazards fully justify the advice that dry-sanding should never be performed indoors for the removal of leaded paint. Burning or other stripping methods using heat can generate lead-rich fumes which may be dangerous to the decorator and occupant if exposed for long periods. Hot-air tools are now widely available, which soften the paint without generating fumes, provided that the temperature is below 500°C, and allows it to be scraped off. However it is quite easy to overheat the paint with these hot air machines set at the lowest level so they must be used with care and there is also the danger of generating lead-rich dust as the machine will blow particles or flakes of paint about as it is being scraped off, causing widespread dust contamination.

Wet sanding avoids the hazards of both dry sanding and burning, but is slow for large areas and messy for domestic purposes. Chemical paint strippers will give satisfactory results, but they are expensive, caustic to the skin and give off fumes which are hazardous if breathed to excess.

One must conclude that there is no completely 'safe' method of removing lead based paints, but in overall terms chemical strippers appear to pose the least hazard, provided adequate ventilation can be assured. It is essential that DIY decorators provide adequate through ventilation. In order to achieve this it is usually necessary to open sufficient windows and doors so that air moves across the whole house while stripping and painting is in progress and also until the paint has dried. (The solvents used in some paints are hazardous if breathed to excess.) Professional decorators should take adequate precautions to protect themselves from dust and fumes using appropriate breathing apparatus.

8.3.3 Dust

Dust is released by alterations and refurbishment of older property and by paint stripping. It is possible that the dust in floor and roof voids together with service ducts may contain raised levels of lead dust due to previous redecoration of high lead content paints and general environmental levels. Care should therefore be exercized, particularly with refurbishment so that all dust is collected by vacuum equipment at each stage of the work and properly disposed of as below. Suitable vacuum clearers are: Nilfisk GS81h and 82h.

8.3.4 Disposal

Lead pipe and sheet has significant scrap value and this will doubtless form one method of disposal in the short term, allowing recycling of the material, but this begs the question of the future. Local authorities will provide advice on the disposal of large quantities of lead waste.

Paint flakes and scrapings together with dust from refurbishment and alterations should be collected in stout, sealed plastic bags and may be disposed of, in small quantities, through the normal local authority waste collection arrangements. Large quantities may require special arrangements to be made with the local authority.

8.4 Useful references

Ainsworth, R.G. *et al* (1977) 'Lead in drinking water'. Water Research Centre Technical report TR43.
Department of the Environment (1977) 'Lead in drinking water — a survey of Great Britain'. Pollution paper No. 12.
Rutter, M. and Russel-Jones, R. (ed) 'Lead versus health: sources and effects of low level lead'. 1983 J. Wiley and Sons.

8.5 Useful addresses

For further advice and information on the lead content in the water supply contact:
    Local Environmental Health Department
    Local Water Authority

For further advice and detailed information on lead in paintwork contact:

Your local Environmental Health Department

Department of the Environment
Room A.3.20
Romney House
Marsham Street
London SW1P 3PY

Scottish Development Department
Room 401
Pentland House
47 Robbs Loan
Edinburgh EH14 1TY

Welsh Office
Room 2115
Cathays Park
Cardiff CF1 3NG

The Paintmakers Association of Great Britain Ltd
Alembic House
93 Albert Embankment
London SE1 7TY

8.6 Conclusion

The steps to be taken when a hazardous material is suspected in an existing building can
be summarized as follows:
Identification
Measurement
Assessment
Sealing
Removal
Disposal

Although this procedure[4] was originally outlined for asbestos it should prove equally
effective for other appropriate materials.

Initial identification of any hazardous material will be made by the building owner,
tenant, surveyor or architect. The function of the building consultants after this phase will
essentially revolve around managing the process and ensuring the best advice is available
to the client. It is essential reliable assistance and guidance is sought either from the local
authority environmental health department or approved private laboratories.

Detailed measurements must be made, using appropriate techniques, to identify
precisely the nature of the material concerned. Exploration and measurement of dust in
wall, floor and roof voids; service ducts etc. may give a useful indication of the presence
of asbestos fibre. Inexperienced observers can mistake asbestos insulation board for certain
of the non-asbestos replacement and as already outlined some types of asbestos are more
hazardous than others, hence the necessity to identify the type.

Assessment of the field data and any laboratory analysis results must attempt to
establish the likely exposure as difficult as this is (see Section I — Introduction) in order to
come to a realistic, informed view on the appropriateness of removal, sealing or other
measures and to balance the various risks involved.

Sealing and removal exercises require careful planning, especially with asbestos to which the public is particularly sensitive due to recent media coverage. Extensive consulations with all parties — local authority, consultants, owners, tenants, trades unions and the local press — is essential to the success of this type of operation. Temporary air locks or housings to control dust emissions and temporary accommodation for occupants may be necessary. This is obviously a very expensive process and should only be entered into when a serious risk is established when detailed planning is required to avoid the unnecessary waste of resources. Ideally such work should be arranged to coincide with major replacement work, e.g. removal of asbestos pipe insulation at boiler replacement, to reduce overall costs to a minimum[5].

Finally, it is essential that a responsible attitude is taken over disposal of the material. If precautions are not observed the problem is just passed on to others and general environmental contamination may result.

When a hazardous material is identified and, as a result of the type of analysis outlined above, it is decided that in the particular location the material is safe, or that after appropriate sealing it can safely remain in place, adequate records must be kept of the discovery and the action taken. In this context the Royal Institution of Chartered Surveyors' recent suggestion of a logbook to record house condition, repair, replacement and other maintenance work would appear to offer the best way of recording such information and allowing it to be passed on to subsequent owners or tenants. It will also be necessary for Building Surveyors, Architects and others responsible for the maintenance and alteration of buildings to include a check for hazardous materials in their survey procedure. It is surprising how little concern is shown about hazardous materials by householders, purchasers surveyors, architects and builders.

[1] Adapted from the 9th Report of Royal Commission on Environmental Pollution, Command Paper 8852, 1983, Section 6—4.

[2] Adapted from DOE Information Note: Lead in Paintwork 1983.

[3] Adapted from the 9th Report of Royal Commission of Environmental Pollution, Command Paper 8852, 1983, Section 6—26.

[4] Adapted from Figure 1, 'Asbestos in Buildings: A Government View', Dr N. King. Paper presented to a seminar — 'Asbestos in Construction', Grosvenor House, London 19.3.84.

[5] 'Housing Management's Approach to the Problems of Asbestos', K.W. Lomas IPFA FIH, Director of Homes and Property Services, Coventry City Council. Paper presented to seminar — Asbestos in Construction', Grosvenor House, London 19.3.84.

Appendix I Lead content of paints

The tests on paints to establish the lead content were carried out by an independent laboratory. It should be noted that only one tin of each paint was sampled and some variation may be expected between different batches of the same paint.

The results given are in the main for 'wet' paint taken from the tin. Some dry film results are also included. Dry films give higher results depending upon the wet : dry film ratio but are of the order of 2 times that of wet.

Attention is drawn to the recommendation in the 9th report of the Royal Commission on environmental pollution that the lead levels in paint should be reduced to 0.06 % (600 parts per million).

It should be noted that at the time of going to press it had been announced on the 27th February 1985 in a parliamentary written answer from Mr William Waldgrave, a Minister for the Environment, that there was now agreement between Government and the industry (paint makers) on the outstanding questions arising out of the recommendations of the Royal Commission's report on Lead in the Environment, and that lead driers will cease to be used in gloss paint, undercoats and related primers for whites and near whites, by 1st January 1986, and for all colours by 1st July 1987.

However, in the meantime the lists of paints shown below can be used as a guide, but forms only a small sample of all the paints available on the market. To reiterate the comments made in the guidance notes in Application 7.23 'Undercoats and finishing paints' the editors asked every company registered with the paintmakers association for the lead content of certain of their paints, but in the main this information was not forthcoming.

Table A1 Primers

	Wet film (ppm)	Dry film (ppm)
Crown Decorative Products Ltd		
Calcium plumbate primer	220,000	—
Primer, multi-purpose primer	150	—
Primer, alkali resisting	110	—
Primer acrylic primer/undercoat white	<20	—
ICI Dulux Products		
Etching primer No 568 (Blue)	122	140
Metal primer red lead	13,000	100,000
Quick drying metal primer zinc phosphate (mustard)	93	245
Metal primer chromate (greeny yellow)	703	3,700
Red lead metal primer BS2523 Type B	11,200	160,000
High opacity primer undercoat (white)	13	30
Metallic primer zinc phosphate (red)	252	2,100
Quick drying grey-green primer A540—157	828	2,760
Quick drying red lead primer	40,800	120,000
Universal primer	23	33
Aluminium sealer and wood primer	11	23
Metal primer calcium plumbate	65,450	85,000
International Paint Protective Coatings Ltd		
Primer for wood, white	1,200	—
Interprimer CPA607 lead	390,000 (non-homogeneous)	—
Donald Macphersons & Co Ltd		
Zinc phosphate metal primer	3,800	—
Universal primer	2,100	—
Aluminium wood primer	<20	—
Zinc chromate metal primer	2,000	—
Manders Paints Ltd		
Universal wood primer, white	2,000	—
Metallic lead primer	99,000	—
Blundell-Permoglaze Ltd		
Acrylic primer/undercoat	<20	—
Red oxide metal primer	3,600	—
Wood primer, pink	2,900	—
Wood and metal primer, pink	1,900	—

Table A2 Undercoats

	Wet film (ppm)	Dry film (ppm)
Crown Decorative Products Ltd		
Acrylic primer/undercoat, white	<20	—
ICI Dulux Products		
Matchmaker undercoat, pastel base (moonbeam)	465	1,500
Matchmaker undercoat, mid-base (charcoal)	518	1,400
Dulux Undercoat, white	22	30
International Paint Protective Coatings Ltd		
Undercoat, white	2,800	—
Manders Paints Ltd		
Undercoat, white VC100	70	—
Blundell-Permoglaze Ltd		
Undercoat, white	1,500	—

Table A3 Gloss Finishing

	Wet film (ppm)	Dry film (ppm)
Crown Decorative Products Ltd		
Gloss — brilliant white	2,600	—
Non-drip gloss, brilliant white	1,800	—
ICI Dulux Products		
Matchmaker, gloss finish, pastel base (moonbeam)	1,472	4,600
Matchmaker gloss finish, deep base (charcoal)	1,292	3,400
International Paint Protective Coatings Ltd		
Gloss finish, brilliant white	2,400	—
Donald Macphersons & Co Ltd		
Gloss, brilliant white	2,700	—
Manders Paints Ltd		
Gloss finish, brilliant white	2,300	—
Non-drip gloss, brilliant white	1,500	—
Polyurethane gloss	1,800	—
Blundell-Permoglaze Ltd		
Gloss, brilliant white	1,900	—

Table A4 Emulsions

	Wet film (ppm)	Dry film (ppm)
Crown Decorative Products Ltd		
Brilliant white matt emulsion	<20	—
Plus two matt vinyl, brilliant white	30	—
Eggshell white	1,850	—
ICI Dulux Products		
Non-drip gloss with silthane (conker)	295	670
Brilliant white non-drip gloss with silthane	27	70
Silthane silk pastel base	17	46
Matchmaker, silthane silk, pastel base (moonbeam)	6	18
Matchmaker, vinyl matt, pastel base (moonbeam)	15	34
Matchmaker, vinyl silk, pastel base (moonbeam)	20	40
Matchmaker, vinyl silk, deep base (charcoal)	12	20
Matchmaker, vinyl matt, deep base (charcoal)	3	6
Trade, Super matt high opacity emulsion (white)	8	15
Trade, Super matt high opacity emulsion (hopsack)	31	60
International Paint Protective Coatings Ltd		
Vinyl emulsion, brilliant white matt	<20	—
Flat finish, white	960	—
Eggshell finish, brilliant white	1,700 (non-homogeneous)	—
Vinyl silk finish, brilliant white	<20	—
Donald Macphersons & Co Ltd		
Wall sheen vinyl silk, brilliant white	<20	—
Eggshell, brilliant white	1,600	—
Emulsion vinyl finish, brilliant white	<20	—
Manders Paints Ltd		
Vinyl matt, brilliant white	<20	—
Eggshell finish, brilliant white	2,100	—
Blundell-Permoglaze Ltd		
Eggshell white	<20	—
Panmastic emulsion, white	<20	—
Panmastic vinyl silk, white	<20	—

Table A5 Varnishes and wood stains

	Wet film (ppm)	Dry film (ppm)
ICI Dulux Products		
Woodcare interior varnish polyurethane, gloss	751	1,670
Woodcare, exterior varnish	532	1,400
Woodcare preservative woodstain (ebony)	13	24
Woodcare preservative woodstain (pine)	24	44
Woodcare preservative basecoat (dark)	10	14
Woodcare preservative basecoat (light)	22	30
Donald Macphersons & Co Ltd		
Wood finish polyurethane, stain	1,100	—

Index

Numbers in bold **7.25** refer to Application Sheet numbers.